A NEW CONSCIOUSNESS,
A NEW PRIDE,
A BOLD NEW LITERARY MOVEMENT

The Mexican-American people and culture
of the United States, so long blanketed by
official neglect and pervasive prejudice, have
undergone a dramatic renaissance in the
past decade. The most visible manifestations
of this emergence were the Delano grape
strike and outbreaks of social protest in
the Southwest—but an equally vital and
fascinating aspect has been a powerful new
literary movement giving memorable voice
to Chicano realities, aspirations, and genius.

ABOUT THE EDITORS

Dr. Dorothy E. Harth is Professor of Spanish
Language and Literature at Onondaga
Community College.

Lewis M. Baldwin is Chairman of the English
Department at Onondaga Community
College.

Other MENTOR Books of Related Interest

VOICES
of
AZTLAN
Chicano Literature
of Today

EDITED BY
Dorothy E. Harth
AND
Lewis M. Baldwin

A MENTOR BOOK
NEW AMERICAN LIBRARY

TIMES MIRROR
NEW YORK AND SCARBOROUGH, ONTARIO
THE NEW ENGLISH LIBRARY LIMITED, LONDON

ACKNOWLEDGMENTS

Alurista, "can this really be the end," "fruto de bronce," "en el barrio," "must be the season of the witch," "in the barrio sopla el viento," and "when raza," from *Floricanto*. Copyright © 1971 by the Regents of the University of California. Reprinted by permission of Alurista.

Raymond Barrio, "Dawn," from *The Plum Plum Pickers*. Copyright © 1969, 1971 by Raymond Barrio. Reprinted by permission of Harper and Row, Inc.

Aristeo Brito, Jr., "El Peregrino." Copyright © 1971 by Aristeo Brito, Jr. Printed by permission of Aristeo Brito, Jr.

Abelardo [Delgado], "El Chisme," El Vendido," "La Causa," and "Stupid America," from *Chicano 25 Pieces of a Chicano Mind*. Reprinted by permission of Abelardo.

Marcus Duran, "Retrato de un Bato Loco." Copyright © 1970 by *Con Safos*, Inc. Reprinted by permission of *Con Safos*, Inc.

"El Chapo," "Chavalo Encanicado." Copyright © 1971 by *Con Safos*, Inc. Reprinted by permission of *Con Safos*, Inc.

Leonardo Elias, "Aztec Mother." Printed by permission of Leonardo Elias.

Ernesto Galarza, from *Barrio Boy*. Copyright © 1971 by the University of Notre Dame Press. Reprinted by permission of the University of Notre Dame Press.

Manual Gomez, "No Se Puede Olvidar," from *El Ombligo*. Copyright © 1971 by Centro de Estudios Chicanos Publications. Reprinted by permission of *El Ombligo*.

Jorge Gonzalez, "A Delano," from *El Ombligo*. Copyright © 1971 by Centro de Estudios Chicanos Publications. Reprinted by permission of *El Ombligo*.

Gallo Kirach, "Tecatos," from *El Ombligo*. Copyright © 1971 by Centro de Estudios Chicanos Publications. Reprinted by permission of *El Ombligo*.

Cesar Lopez, "Católicos por La Raza," from *El Ombligo*. Copyright © by Centro de Estudios Chicanos Publications. Reprinted by permission of *El Ombligo*.

Amado Muro, "Sunday in Little Chihuahua." Copyright © 1965 by *New Mexico Quarterly*. Reprinted by permission of Amado Muro.

Amado Muro, "Maria Tepache." Copyright © 1969 by *Arizona Quarterly*. Reprinted by permission of Amado Muro.

Jerónimo G. Ortega, "Blue Bike Brings a Blue Day." Copyright © 1970 by *Con Safos*, Inc. Reprinted by permission of *Con Safos*, Inc.

Gloria Perez, "Mi Hombre," from *El Ombligo*. Copyright © 1971

(The following page constitutes an extension of this copyright page.)

MENTOR TRADEMARK REG. U.S. PAT. OFF. AND FOREIGN COUNTRIES
REGISTERED TRADEMARK—MARCA REGISTRADA
HECHO EN CHICAGO, U.S.A.

SIGNET, SIGNET CLASSICS, MENTOR, PLUME and MERIDIAN BOOKS are published *in the United States* by The New American Library, Inc., 1301 Avenue of the Americas, New York, New York 10019, *in Canada* by The New American Library of Canada Limited, 81 Mack Avenue, Scarborough, 704, Ontario, *in the United Kingdom* by The New English Library Limited, Barnard's Inn, Holborn, London E.C. 1, England

First Printing, June, 1974

1 2 3 4 5 6 7 8 9

PRINTED IN THE UNITED STATES OF AMERICA

03226

Contents

Introduction

If one were to consult almost any anthology of Colonial American literature, one would find no mention of the early Spanish explorers and pioneers of the Southwest. Instead, in almost every case, our American literature textbooks begin with selections by William Bradford and Captain John Smith. The justification for this exclusion of the early Spanish writers is usually that they were not truly "American," but were, rather, Spanish or perhaps Mexican. Yet this logic is fallacious as Bradford and Smith were, after all, English, the former a settler, to be sure, but in an English colony that was not to become the United States for 150 years, and the latter an Englishman who returned to England after each voyage of discovery and chose to die there. Nor is the argument that the Spanish chroniclers did not produce literature a valid one, as most Colonial American writing was not "literature" in any real sense, but chronicles, diaries, travelogues, and sermons. Yet through the use of these specious arguments the once dominant and still important culture of California and the Southwest, a culture typified by the blending of Spanish and Indian traditions, has been overlooked, not only by literary historians but by the larger society itself for nearly four hundred years.

This Anglo-Saxon-centered attitude on the part of most Americans might make some sense if the area under discussion had remained in Spanish or, later, Mexican hands. Yet under the Treaty of Guadalupe Hidalgo of 1848, a treaty imposed by conquest upon our Mexican neighbor, all of the Mexican land north of the Rio Grande was ceded to the United States. The treaty contained specific guarantees for the indigenous peoples of the area, largely Mexican or Indian, of respect for their culture and their property rights. Like the Indian treaties; however, those guarantees were seldom if ever honored, and even today Reies Tijerina is attempting to force the state and federal governments to abide by the treaty obligations. Still, throughout the 175 years that have elapsed since these peoples became United States citizens, their lot has remained much the same: quiet, pastoral, and largely poverty ridden. In this century thousands of these Mexican-American citizens have migrated to the cities in search of a better life, but in the cities they have by and large been relegated to those menial tasks afforded our more visible minorities in this country, while being housed in crowded barrios, the "sunshine slums" of California and the Southwest. Furthermore, despite a viable and long-established Spanish language press, the Mexican-American has remained, in America, largely an invisible minority except when stereotypically portrayed and exploited as a sleeping peon on a neon motel signboard, or hustling corn chips on television commercials.

Since the end of World War II, however, the "sleeping peon" of the motel sign has awakened, stretched, and in testing his strength, has found it effective. Called to defend his country, he left the barrios of East Los Angeles, Denver, Tucson, Albuquerque, San Antonio, and El Paso, as well as thousands of rural campos, for the various theaters of World War II. When he returned, and a disproportionate number of his brothers did not return, it was with the realization that the freedom he had defended from the Axis enemy did not in fact exist for the Mexican-American, a situation he would no longer accept. And, while he was gone, his younger brother may have become a pachuco. This phenomenon, despite its undesirable connotations in the minds of Anglo-Americans and older Mexican-Americans, celebrated for the first time the uniqueness of being "brown," of being Mexican-American or of Mexican ancestry. It denied the entrenched American myth of acculturation, the fond chimera that held that learning the English language and the Constitution by rote made one a 100 percent American and automatically as good as the next guy. Yet the pachuco movement was not a wholly positive force, however, as in some respects it was a way for the members of the gang to withdraw from both societies, a negation of hope, and a hostile and self-conscious alienation from everyone and everything but the members of the gang. Yet it would seem that these two experiences coalesced in the minds and consciences of Americans of Mexican or Spanish ancestry and helped to shape a distinct identity, a heritage, a belief in self. This new attitude was distinctly different from the phony "Days of the Dons" festivals of California and the Southwest where everyone pretended, for a day, that all Mexicans were the blue-blooded descendants of the old Spanish grandees, and for the remaining 364 days of the year pretended that Mexican-Americans didn't exist. Thus, by the time of the outbreak of the Korean War, the hyphenated Mexican-American had become a Chicano, and proud of it.

The origin of the term *Chicano* is unclear, but by the 1950s the term had gained wide currency among Mexican-Americans in the United States as the term for a native-born United States citizen of Mexican-American or Mexican parentage. Some Mexican-Americans resist the title, preferring their older hyphenated identity, but by and large the term *Chicano* is a proud title worn by Americans of Latin-Indian ancestry. Together with other ethnic minorities, they are today demanding the right to a pluralistic culture that will recognize both their fundamental rights as American citizens and their particular ethnic heritage and traditions. It could be said, then, that the term *Chicano* is, for the younger Mexican-American, more than simply a term for one's ethnic origin or cultural identity, as it stands also for an active political consciousness that will no longer tolerate second-class citizenship.

The Chicano has a tripartite cultural heritage: the heritage of *Aztlan*, the Indian past; the heritage also of his Spanish and Mexican antecedents; and finally, the "American" heritage of the Anglo-centered culture to which he had had to adapt. It is perhaps this tripartite heritage that typified the event that brought worldwide, if terribly belated, attention to Chicano problems: the *huelga* or strike of 1965 against the grape growers around Delano, California. Led by Cesar Chavez, the *huelga* probably owed its ultimate success to his masterful combination of the American labor union tactics of the strike and boycott, the traditional Mexican pattern of family solidarity (whole families struck together, as they had picked together, and were able to convince all their relatives and friends to do likewise), and the religious fervor generated by the Virgin of Guadalupe, patron of the Mexican. By skillfully combining these three elements of the Chicano heritage: Yankee-style economic clout, traditional Mexican-American family unity, and the deep Roman Catholic faith of the majority of his people, Chavez led his farm workers, under the *huelga* eagle and preceded by a statue of the Brown Virgin, on the long march to Sacramento and to ultimate victory. The victory for Chavez's people was more than an economic one, as it forced the growers, and in some sense the world at large, to at last recognize the essential humanity of these workers.[1]

We have attempted to bring together in this book the voice of the Chicano people, as it is available in Chicano literature from World War II until the present. It is all "contemporary" writing because we honestly think that Chicano literature, as differentiated from Latin-American, Mexican, or Mexican-American literatures, necessarily developed apace with Chicano identity, a phenomenon we have traced from the war years to the present time. Before World War II there apparently were few, if any, outlets for the Chicano writer: his productions were limited either to a conservative Spanish-language press, the oral tradition of the barrio and the campo, or, pruned and Anglicized beyond recognition as Chicano, made over for general consumption. This unfortunate situation has happily been reversed in recent years. There are literally hundreds of Chicano periodicals (although like the little magazines of the thirties they have rather sporadic life-spans), together with some substantial and important periodicals such as *Con Safos, El Grito,* and *La Raza.* Additionally, Chicano publishing houses are beginning to spring up, such as Mictla Publications, Origines Publications, and the excellent Quinto Sol press. Finally, universities and colleges, especially in California and Texas, recognizing finally the untouched reservoir that is Chicano culture, have recently established several centers for Chicano studies.

Some sociologists and cultural anthropologists, citing the preponderance of poverty and the generally low level of educational achievement among Chicanos, attribute the small volume of literary production by Chicanos to economic and educational factors. As briefly mentioned above, we do not accept this rationale. It seems a hollow generalization based upon misinformation and ignorance, and we hope this volume will help dispel that myth. Literary en-

---

[1] César Chavez "The Organizer's Tale," *Ramparts,* July 1966, pp. 43-50.

deavors are not limited exclusively to the well educated or to the affluent, but unfortunately access to publication often is, and the apparent cultural and literary renaissance of the Chicanos today is due more to their newly found militancy and a belated "discovery" by Anglo-Americans than to any suddenly acquired literacy. Another problem with Chicano literature is that much of it, quite naturally, has been in Spanish, and has thus been unrecognized or disregarded by literary critics and historians because it was difficult to "classify." Yet all races at all times produce poets, and the Chicano, with his great heritage of Spanish and Indian mysticism, has in all probability produced more than his share. The Chicano poet has not found a voice, he has found listeners.

Literature, because it often involves a journey of discovery in the tradition of the epic and the romance, can be as epic in scope as Chavez's long march to Sacramento. The *huelga,* for many Americans, resulted in the discovery of an hitherto unknown people in their midst, *La Raza.* One important dimension of a people that can be measured is their culture, which quite often is a concern for identity as reflected in art. In these pages we have attempted to bring together the best in Chicano literature, in all common genres. We have established just two criteria: one, the criterion of literary merit, a universal standard that respects no ethnic boundaries and which insists that although some literature may also be propaganda, mere propaganda is not literature. The second criterion, established perhaps arbitrarily, is that this literature reflect the voice and condition of the Chicano artist living in the contemporary United States.

Reluctantly, we have limited the selections in this volume to works written in English, knowing full well that this action necessarily excludes a large body of excellent work by Chicano authors. Yet we feel that it is nevertheless necesssary at this time, because our major aim and purpose, if indeed not our sole one, is to bring representative and contemporary Chicano literature to the attention of the widest possible audience.

We have arranged this volume according to genres; short fiction, selections from novels, poetry, and finally, drama. Our hope is to be as representative as possible, while at the same time whetting the reader's appetite so that he will seek out and read the complete works of the authors included.

To show the development and direction of Chicano literature from World War II to the present, we have arranged
the materials in a loose chronological order within each
genre.

DOROTHY E. HARTH
Professor of Spanish

LEWIS M. BALDWIN
Associate Professor of English

Onondaga Community College
1972

I

Contemporary
Chicano
Prose Fiction

Introduction

Our first selection, "El Hoyo," by Mario Suarez, is a compassionate description of the folk and folkways of a Tucson barrio. Written in 1947, the author reminisces about the area, using conventional narrative structure and an omniscient point of view. Yet the sketch is not merely a piece of nostalgia, as it contains deep sociological and philosophical insight into those lives it sketches, and the tone is adamant in its insistence upon the cultural multiplicity to be found among the Chicanos of the barrio.

The next selection, "Sunday in Little Chihuahua," by Amado Muro, treats, as its title asserts, life in the Chicano barrio of El Paso, Texas. Told in conventional narrative style in the first person, Muro is concerned with life in the barrio and what made it significant. There is a notable difference, though, between the barrios of "El Hoyo" and "Little Chihuahua." While the Tucson barrio seems isolated, cut off, and its people alienated from the outside world if not, certainly, from one another, the people of Little Chihuahua look to Mexico as their cultural "home." The Chicano's dualism is a significant theme in much Chicano literature: he sees himself as having a double citizenship, his economic one in the United States, his cultural one in Mexico.

Our other selection of Muro's work, "Mariá Tepache," restates this theme of cultural duality. The heroine of the story, Mariá Tepache, runs a combination grocery store/restaurant in San Antonio that is a haven for the poor of *La Raza,* an oasis of chili peppers and warmth in an area that, despite its large numbers of Chicano people, seems nevertheless Yanqui and hostile. The significant theme in this tale is that Muro shows that for Mariá the Chicano ways of caring for one's brother outweight the Anglo business ethic.

"Zeta"'s "Perla Is a Pig," is another treatment of a rural barrio. The dialogue, in English with the exception of some *pocho* interjections, is a careful rendition of the speech of uneducated Chicanos as the story sketches with bitter truth life in a poverty-stricken village with all its attendant ignorance and fear. Yet there is high humor in the story, part of it bitter irony, part burlesque, and part just plain comic: the race it laughs at is the human one.

"Retrato de un Bato Loco," by Marcus Duran, is a significant piece of work, highly innovative in both content and form. It is the story of the last day in the life of a Los Angeles heroin addict. Although its subject is of great sociological significance, there is no preaching in Duran's piece, no moralizing, no sanctimonious "I told you so's," just the ugly end. Moreover, the narrative structure or dialogue in the story is entirely in the *vato* dialect, an extremely difficult one to render into English.

The next selection, "On the Road to Texas: Pete Fonseca," by Tomas Rivera, is a half-sad and half-comic account of the impact of Pete Fonseca on a rural barrio. Told from the point of view of a small Chicano boy who is very impressed by Pete initially—"we finally decided that he was at least half pachuco"—the reader soon learns that Pete is a small-time hustler who loves, and ultimately leaves, "La Chata." The boy's naïveté reflects the naïveté of the villagers, who are taken in by Pete's line. Pete may symbolically represent the exploiter, the cheap *vendido* who exploits his own people for private gain, or he may simply represent a type familiar to us all, the sweet talker whom we believe because we want to, knowing all the while we are being used.

The next two stories move from the rural campos into the barrios of Los Angeles. "Chavalo Encanicado," by "El Chapo" is a tale of adolescent love in the barrio. Told in the *vato* dialect as rendered into English, it is a hilarious story of true love frustrated. Our hero must pluck innumerable chickens for his mother's business shortly before his first "date," with a girl he has admired from afar. He is further, and finally, frustrated by a suspicious father. The significance, aside from the fact that the incident involved seems much like the equally hilarious fence-painting scene in *Tom Sawyer,* lies in the sociological mix of American adolescent behavioral patterns and old Mexico family tradition, where the girls are guarded like precious jewels.

"Blue Bike Brings a Blue Day," by Jerónimo G. Ortega relates a much more tragic tale of life in the barrio, told from the point of view of a small Chicano boy, who learns that there is no room for innocence in the barrio. Upon rebuilding a bicycle from parts he found in a trash can, the child learns that the Anglo world considers him a thief, not because he steals, but simply because he is brown, a Chicano. How will this shape Chinto's idea of self? We cannot know, of course, but one suspects that any society that brands certain ethnic minorities as criminals should not be surprised when some of those people feel they have nothing to lose in turning to lawlessness.

Barrio Boy is the story of one family's flight north from Mexico at the time of the Revolution of 1912, when thousands of Mexican people fled north to seek the relative quiet and safety of *Los Estados Unidos*. The narrator relates the story, beginning from his memories as a small child when the family arrived, and his subsequent growing up in the States. The book, although formally an autobiography, stresses a point that is almost universally valid: the importance and closeness of family ties among Mexican and Mexican-American peoples. Each crisis is encountered not by the individual involved, but by the family as a whole, and is met and dealt with by the family. As the children become more and more Anglicized, while the family moves from tiny Mexican village to Texas border barrio and finally to home ownership in California, some quite obvious and some very subtle changes take place. The book is important, we feel, because it gives an extended insight into life in the barrio and the Mexican-American family.

José Villarreal's novel, *Pocho*, is similarly an account of growing up in the Chicano communities in California and the Southwest. Once again, the importance of family ties is stressed, as is the cultural shock of Anglicization. The mother adopts "Anglo" independent ways, much to the father's distress; he leaves home to seek solace with a younger "Mexican" girl, while the Yankee stress on money drives the narrator's sisters out of the home. Essentially, the entire novel is the tale of the dissolution of an ancient cultural tradition upon the shoals of the "American Way of Life," an honest and often brutal account of the results of "Americanization," and so, in some ways, a book that champions the cause of cultural plurality. We have selected that portion of the novel that seems most representative of the central conflict, but suggest that the reader see the book in its entirety.

Chicano, by Richard Vasquez, departs from the family history motif of the above books through the use of a dramatic plot to point up an incidence of contemporary cultural conflict. The major focus of the novel is a love story about a Chicana, Mariana, and her Anglo sociology-major boyfriend, David. The plot, evocative of similar ones including *Romeo and Juliet* and *West Side Story,* demonstrates that love does not conquer all and that in real life our built-in prejudices often defeat it. Ironically, David later finds out that Mariana is not a "Mexican" but a descendant of one of the original California families and thus quite acceptable as a bride to his parents and society at large. This is of course a satirical comment by the author on our hypocritical attitudes and the phoniness of the "Days of the Dons" in Southern California. Yet David is a weak character and may well have run from any responsibility; the novel may be pointing up the sad fact that racism is often an excuse to avoid our human responsibilities. Vasquez traces the lives of not only the two protagonists, but the lives of all the members of Mariana's family and friends who experience on a multitude of levels the frustrations, tragedies, and even occasional delights of Chicano life in present-day California. The section that we include deals not just with David and Mariana, but with a fiesta that is a fine portrait of the Chicano community at leisure, or attempted leisure.

The last selection from a contemporary novel is Chapter 10 from Raymond Barrio's *The Plum Plum Pickers.* Set in a representative migrant labor camp in California, it describes the dust, the filth, and the wretchedness that permeate the camp and that rub off, literally and figuratively, upon all of those involved in it. Barrio's prose style, with its use of the stream-of-consciousness technique, bits of newspaper clippings, lines by Anglo radio announcers, and popular Mexican songs, as well as its images of the oppressive dust and heat, is reminiscent at times of Faulkner, at times of Dos Passos. Barrio's vision of life in the campo is a nightmare—a nightmare experienced in reality by the camp boss—composed of surreal awakenings to the clash of thrown garbage-can lids inscribed "J. Murrietta" in chalk (for Joaquin Murrietta, the Chicano Robin Hood of old California), together with wine-clouded visions of man's hungers, his empty belly, his empty pockets, his empty life. All of this is seen through the sweat-clouded eyes of the pickers and the greed-clouded ones of the boss, who finally awakens to the real-life nightmare of his lynching by dim Chicano faces in the dark.

El Hoyo

Mario Suarez

From the center of downtown Tucson the ground slopes gently away to Main Street, drops a few feet, and then rolls to the banks of the Santa Cruz River. Here lies the sprawling section of the city known as El Hoyo. Why it is called El Hoyo is not clear. It is not a hole as its name would imply; it is simply the river's immediate valley. Its inhabitants are *chicanos* who raise hell on Saturday night, listen to Padre Estanislao on Sunday morning, and then raise more hell on Sunday night. While the term *chicano* is the short way of saying *Mexicano,* it is the long way of referring to everybody. Pablo Gutierrez married the Chinese grocer's daughter and acquired a store; his sons are *chicanos.* So are the sons of Killer Jones who threw a fight in Harlem and fled to El Hoyo to marry Cristina Mendez. And so are all of them—the assortment of harlequins, bandits, oppressors, oppressed, gentlemen, and bums who came from Old Mexico to work for the Southern Pacific, pick cotton, clerk, labor, sing, and go on relief. It is doubtful that all of these spiritual sons of Mexico live in El Hoyo because they love each other—many fight and bicker constantly. It is doubtful that the *chicanos* live in El Hoyo because of its scenic beauty—it is everything but beautiful. Its houses are built of unplastered adobe, wood, license plates, and abandoned car parts. Its narrow streets are mostly clearings which have, in time, acquired names. Except for the tall trees which nobody has ever cared to identify, nurse, or destroy, the main things known to grow in the general area are weeds, garbage piles, dogs, and kids. And it is doubtful that the *chicanos* live in El Hoyo because it is safe—many times the Santa Cruz River has risen and inundated the area.

In other respects living in El Hoyo has its advantages. If one is born with the habit of acquiring bills, El Hoyo is where the bill collectors are less likely to find you. If one has acquired the habit of listening to Señor Perea's Mexican

Hour in the wee hours of the morning with the radio on at full blast, El Hoyo is where you are less likely to be reported to the authorities. Besides, Perea is very popular and to everybody sooner or later is dedicated The Mexican Hat Dance. If one has inherited a bad taste for work but inherited also the habit of eating, where, if not in El Hoyo, are the neighbors more willing to lend you a cup of flour or beans? When Señora Garcia's house burned to the ground with all her belongings and two kids, a benevolent gentleman conceived the gesture that put her on the road to solvency. He took five hundred names and solicited from each a dollar. At the end of the week he turned over to the heartbroken but grateful señora three hundred and fifty dollars in cold cash and pocketed his recompense. When the new manager of a local business decided that no more Mexican girls were to work behind his counters, it was the *chicanos* of El Hoyo who acted as pickets and, on taking their individually small but collectively great buying power elsewhere, drove the manager out and the girls returned to their jobs. When the Mexican Army was enroute to Baja California and the *chicanos* found out that the enlisted men ate only at infrequent intervals they crusaded across town with pots of beans, trays of tortillas, boxes of candy, and bottles of wine to meet the train. When someone gets married celebrating is not restricted to the immediate families and friends of the couple. The public is invited. Anything calls for a celebration and in turn a celebration calls for anything. On Armistice Day there are no fewer than half a dozen fights at the Tira-Chancla Dance Hall. On Mexican Independence Day more than one flag is sworn allegiance to and toasted with gallon after gallon of Tumba Yaqui.

And El Hoyo is something more. It is this something more which brought Felipe Ternero back from the wars after having killed a score of Germans with his body resembling a patch-work quilt. It helped him to marry a fine girl named Julia. It brought Joe Zepeda back without a leg from Luzon and helps him hold more liquor than most men can hold with two. It brought Jorge Casillas, a gunner flying B-24's over Germany, back to compose boleros. Perhaps El Hoyo is the proof that those people exist who, while not being against anything, have as yet failed to observe the more popular modes of human conduct. Perhaps the humble appearance of El Hoyo justifies the discerning shrugs of more than a few people only vaguely aware of its existence. Perhaps El Hoyo's simplicity motivates many a *chicano* to move far away from its intoxicating *frenesi,* its dark narrow streets, and its shrieking children, to deny the blood-well from which he springs, to claim the blood of a conquistador while his hair is straight and his face beardless. Yet El Hoyo is not the desperate outpost of a few families against the world. It fights for no causes except those which soothe its immediate angers. It laughs and cries with the same amount of passion in times of plenty and of want.

Perhaps El Hoyo, its inhabitants, and its essence can best be explained by telling you a little bit about a dish called *capirotada.* Its origin is uncertain. But it is made of old, new, stale, and hard bread. It is sprinkled with water and then it is cooked with raisins, olives, onions, tomatoes, peanuts, cheese, and general leftovers of that which is good and bad. It is seasoned with salt, sugar, pepper, and sometimes chili or tomato sauce. It is fired with tequila or sherry wine. It is served hot, cold, or just "on the weather" as they say in El Hoyo. The Garcias like it one way, the Quevedos another, the Trilos another, and the Ortegas still another. While in general appearance it does not differ much from one home to another it tastes different everywhere. Nevertheless it is still *capirotada.* And so it is with El Hoyo's *chicanos.* While many seem to the undiscerning eye to be alike it is only because collectively they are referred to as *chicanos.* But like *capirotada,* fixed in a thousand ways and served on a thousand tables, which can only be evaluated by individual taste, the *chicanos* must be so distinguished.

Sunday in Little Chihuahua

Amado Muro

When I was a boy, not long up from Parral, I lived with my uncle Rodolfo Avitia, my mother Amada Avitia de Muro, and my sisters Consuelo and Dulce Nombre de María in El Paso's "Little Chihuahua" quarter.

Next door to the blockhouse tenement in which we lived was a tiny cafe called La Perla de Jalisco. This cafe was run by Doña Antonia Olvera, a jolly and industrious woman from Guadalajara nicknamed Tona la Tapatía.

Doña Antonia kept busy all day long, humming a Guadalajareña while she worked. Her cafe specialized in dishes seldom found elsewhere in Little Chihuahua.

Tona la Tapatía served the sugar tamales that make Oaxaqueños' mouths water. She also made the delicate, wispy tortillas, the biggest and thinnest in all Mexico, that are among the great prides of Sonora. When a countryman tired of eating the thick, freckled flour tortillas made by Chihuahua housewives, he would go to La Perla for an agreeable change, secure in the knowledge that not even the tortilla factories could equal Doña Antonia's products in fineness or texture.

Then, too, Tona served café con leche just as they do in Mexico City cafes, with each cup of coffee more than half-filled with boiling milk. Where, if not to La Perla, would a countryman seeking a cup of hot champurrado go on a cold winter night? And was anyone ever known to impugn the quality of the pancitas which Doña Antonia put into her steaming menudo, a dish known to every Chicano as the only sure cure for a hangover?

La Perla de Jalisco was a neat and clean cafe. On each immaculate table a small dish of chile bravo could always be found and over the front door hung a picture of Juventino Rosas, who besides being the composer of Sobre las Olas, was a tapatío himself.

At a front table Tona's husband, Don Ignacio Olvera, sat all day long with his philosophy books, and his bullring

[16]

reviews stacked up in neat piles before him. He was the president of the José y Juan bullfight club, and also acted as border correspondent for El Redondel, a bullfight magazine published in Mexico City. For his literary services, Don Ignacio received no money at all. But he did obtain passes to the corridas in Ciudad Juárez and the satisfaction of seeing the name "I. Olvera, corresponsal" at the end of his numerous and popular articles.

Between his exhaustive studies of Plato, whom he referred to as the Divine Greek, and his equally exhaustive studies of the matador Rafael Gómez "El Gallo," whom he referred to as the Divine Baldhead, he managed to earn a scholar's reputation for himself in the quarter.

Don Ignacio Olvera was a short, pudgy man with deeply imbedded eyes that kept blinking constantly as though trying to beat their way out of the morass of soggy flesh that surrounded them. His cheekbones were smothered beneath puffs of suety skin that made his round face appear boneless. To Little Chihuahua's genteel residents he was known as the Panzón because of his bobbling paunch. But the quarter's more robust residents knew him as Nalgas de Aplauso, a nickname inspired by his elephantine hips which swayed like a woman's when he walked.

Don Ignacio sat in the cafe all day long playing Novillero and Agustín Lara's Silverio over and over again on the jukebox while he pored over metaphysical disquisitions and bullfight reviews, gathering material for his long articles dealing with past and present bullfighters. He also wrote poems dedicated to Mexican matadores and these, too, were published in El Redondel.

Where was the boy in Little Chihuahua who could not recite the verse about the way Andrés Blando killed the bull Cuatro Milpas with one of the mightiest sword thrusts ever seen in the Ciudad Juárez Plaza?

On that day Don Ignacio Olvera wrote:

> Andrés Blando ha descubierto
> Una manera de herir
> Que no la comprende nadie
> Ni es facil de definir.

And what Little Chihuahua aficionado did not know by heart the satirical ballad he composed on the day the unhappy novilleros Juan Estrada "Gallo" and Jose Lagares "El Piti" heard the three warning bugles and underwent

the humiliation of seeing novillos they could not kill returned to the corrals by the trained oxen?

Of that unlucky day, Don Ignacio had written:

> No quiero carne del toro
> Que Lagares no mató.
> La quiero del de Gallito
> Que vivo se lo dejó.

But despite the popularity of his poems, it was generally
agreed that Don Ignacio's renown rested on a foundation
of solid prose. His most famous article was written on the
day the matador Luis Castro, nicknamed "El Milician de
Mixcoac," cut the ears, tail, and hoof of the great bull
Mariposa from the San Diego de Los Padres herd. He
described the performance thus:

"Luis Castro fights with the gaiety and the abandon of
the gypsies who dance nude amid flowering lemon trees in
Sevilla's joyous San Bernardo quarter, where the great
torero Pepe Luis Vázquez was born. He smiles at the bull
as Othello would have smiled had his blindness not kept
him from seeing that his Desdemona was faithful. His
vibrant cape rises in a harmonious curve like the swallows
which make their nests in the eaves of the Church of Omnia
Santorum where Juan Belmonte, the Triana Earthquake,
was baptized.

"Plato nailed to the door of his Academy the disconcert-
ing words 'None Shall Enter Without Knowing Geometry.'
And by his work with the cape and muleta today our
great military man of the bullring won the right to enter
the Divine Greek's Academy unchallenged. The red ellipses
of his interminable derechazos, the moving and deeply
poetic circumference of his pase de pecho, the semicircular
tragedy of his larga cordobesa, showed us that Luis Castro,
too, knows geometry.

"Today our valiant soldier proved that his heart is as
big and round as that great gypsy moon of which the
unlucky poet García Lorca has sung. So he conquered the
noble bull Mariposa, who, like all true ribbon bulls, had
flies on his face and defenses like the branches of the
milennial ahuehuete trees in Chapultepec Park.

"Thales de Mileto would have said his movement with
the cape represented a perfect conjugation of music and
geometry. A poet like Ronsard would have said that the
rhythm of our soldier's muleta was like the agile and

beautiful flight of a bird. Becquer would have said its magic was that of a ballad heard in the mysterious depths of the Moruno Quarter of Santa Cruz de Sevilla at three in the morning, the hour when the gypsies' hearts stop beating. For Luis Castro's muleta has that suave sweep of which the great Nicaraguan poet has spoken.

"Amiable readers, today I have learned that the smell of a brilliant bullfighter is overpowering. That is because it is impregnated with the odor of greatness. When I saw Luis Castro's farol de rodillas, I thought that the great Rodolfo Gaona, our beloved Caliph of Leó, had come out of retirement to tread the sands of the bullring once more. Marian Azuela was born to be a great novelist. Rafael de Urbino was born to be a great painter. And the 'Mixcoac Militiaman' was born to be a great matador.

"Luis Castro, my hand is extended to you. You have brought a new sense of joy, a new sense of danger to the ancient art of Cúchares. Matador, I salute you. Olé, for the profession of the thousand marvels, the most beautiful of all the fiestas."

On Sundays after the eight o'clock Mass at the Church of San Juan de Los Lagos was over, the children of our neighborhood attended the Pachangas put on by Don Ignacio.

This was held in the corral behind the Perla de Jalisco. Don Ignacio would get out the brilliant cape which Luis Castro had presented him in gratitude for his encomiastic article. He also got out a muleta which had been given him by the matador Carlos Vera "Canitas" in appreciation for an article in which he had compared the young bullfighter's execution of the lasernista pass to that of its inventor, Victoriano de la Serna himself.

On the mornings of the Pachangas, Don Ignacio was nervous as the bullfighters who await their turns in Mexico City's Cuator Caminos Plaza. On the nights before, he stiffened his cape with fish jelly and on windy Sundays he weighted down his muleta with wet sand.

For his Pachangas, Don Ignacio had trained a chow dog he called Mariachi to charge like a bull. He had taught the dog to follow the sway of Luis Castro's cape and Carlos Vera's muleta just as a real bull would do. The dog Mariachi was named after a famous bull from the Corlome herd.

On the blistering Sundays when Mariachi was listless and

came to the lures sluggishly, Don Ignacio heaped insults upon him.

"Son of a bad cow," he reviled him. "Solemn manso, blind burro, Little Sister of Charity."

But on the cold winter Sundays when the dog's body was throbbing with vigor and he came to the lures with a straight and true charge, Don Ignacio praised him extravagantly.

"This is a great and intelligent bull, a rich bonbon from the Corlome herd," he gravely informed the children. "Chamacos, I tell you this brave bull de bandera knows Latin, Greek, German, Sanskrit, and Caló."

Don Ignacio wore bullfighting pumps during the Pachangas. An ancient montera—battered and frizzled—surmounted his massive head. He cited the dog by patting the hardpan earth with his slippered feet.

"Ay, toro," he bellowed at the top of his lungs. "Ven acá, little pear in sweet sauce."

The dog Mariachi, long since grown accustomed to the vagaries of Don Ignacio's mercurial temperament, would look up at his globular master with a resigned expression. Then after a moment he would begin to paw at the earth with his hind legs just as a real bull would do.

"Ay va por ustedes," Don Ignacio would then yell as the dog charged the cape his corpulent master held behind him in the beautiful style invented by Romero Freg.

The delighted children would crown each pass with an Olé. They whooped and hollered hilariously when Don Ignacio, puffing and wheezing lowered himself to his pudgy knees in order to excute the dangerous cambio a Porto Gayola.

Don Ignacio always explained the origin of every lance and pass to the excited spectators.

"Muchachitos, this one is la Saltillera. It is so called because it was created by our great countryman, Fermín Espinoza, 'Armillita,' also known as the Maestro of Saltillo."

Most of us had been going to the Pachangas so long we knew all the lances and passes by heart.

"You, Macario Bueno," Don Ignacio would shout. "Tell me, who created the Sanjuanera and how did this pass get its name?"

"Luis Procuna, El Berrendito de San Juan de Letrán, invented the pass," a small, poorly dressed boy would answer from somewhere in the crowd. "He called it la sanjuanera because he sold tacos in the San Juan de Letrán section in the capital."

Don Ignacio always ended the Pachangas with a suicidal pass of his own invention which he had named la olverina. This pass resembled an inverted manoletina in which the bullfighter stands with his back to the bull. For years Don Ignacio had been trying to persuade some of Mexico's most noted bullfighters to try it out in the ring. But, recognizing the pass as a certain passport to eternity, they had courteously but consistently refused.

After the Pachangas were over, Don Ignacio always started for the back door of the cafe, ostensibly to wash himself down with estropajo. But the clamorous cries of the children and the shouts of the men and women massed on the balconies of the adjacent tenements never failed to bring him back.

"The ballad, Don Nacho," the crowd yelled. "The ballad of Niño de la Palma."

"Ay María, madre mía," Don Ignacio complained every Sunday. "Muchachitos, it's hot as three o'clock in Acapulco, and I swear by our sainted Guadalupana, the Señora of all the world and the Mother of the Mexicans, that I've got to dress for the bullfight."

But the children and the men and women always disregarded his protests. "The ballad, Don Nacho," they hollered. "Recite the ballad."

Don Ignacio always ended by shrugging his shoulders and waving everyone into silence. He would take off the dusty montera, throw his head back, and square his shoulders. His stentorian voice, quivering with emotion, pierced the air like a flamenco singer's cry.

All of us had learned poems by Longfellow in the American school, all of us had learned poems by Juan de Dios Peza and Antonio Plaza in our homes, but at that age of our lives no poem we had known could make our hearts beat as fast as did Las Chuflillas del Niño de la Palma.

With the throbbing intensity of his bass voice, Don Ignacio could make us all see the Ronda bullfighter, son of a shoemaker and once poor like ourselves, in his great hour of victory at Vista Alegre on the day when the Bank of Spain opened its doors to him. He could make us all hear the cry of the Niño, drunk with the exultation of his triumph, as he called to the brave Campo Varela bull, challenging the fierce animal to charge and catch him.

Vengas o no en busca mía
Torillo, mala persona,
Dos cirios y una corona
Tendrás en la enfermería
Que alegría
Cógeme, torillo fiero
Qué salero.

The deafening applause would rise over the corral in a thundering tympany. The children would sing and whistle the quick gay Diana. At the Pachangas even the most melancholy children were laughing and happy. Once I remember seeing Juana de la Torre there. She was the ugliest girl in our school, so ugly that even the gentlest girls in our class taunted her and called her Juana la Marrana. But on the day I saw her there at the Pachanga she was laughing. I could never remember seeing her laugh before.

There, too, I saw Guillermo Díaz. Ordinarily Memo Díaz looked tired and sad. He was then eleven years old and he lived in an earthen-floored casucha with eight other members of his family. Already he had spent a year in the city-county hospital tuberculosis ward. But at the Pachanga that day Memo's face was radiant.

After the recitation was over, the crowds of jubilant children began to disperse. Standing at the back door of the cafe, Don Ignacio watched until the last child was gone. I remember him best as he stood there with a smile on his face.

Many years later when I was a young man of twenty, I sat in La Buena Fe shoe shop and heard my big, burly uncle Rodolfo defend Don Ignacio against two of our countrymen who were bitterly damning him as a preposterous poseur, a drone, and a parasite, a ratero who lived off his wife.

"Cállense, sons of the Great Seven," my aroused uncle told them at last.

He stormed out of the shoe shop and I followed him. We walked down South Stanton Street toward Ciudad Juárez slowly. And I asked my uncle Rodolfo why he had defended Don Ignacio Olvera against charges that were only too true, and why he had become so angry.

My uncle Rodolfo looked at me with a sheepish expression. He started to tell me and then suddenly stopped. He took off his big Zacatecas sombrero, and ran his hand through his gray hair.

"Qué caray," my uncle said, flushing with the embarrassment of his struggle to express an emotion that I am sure he considered unmanly.

He kept his brown face averted from mine. After a moment he got the words out.

"Son," my uncle Rodolfo said slowly without looking at me. "It is just that Don Nacho can make children laugh."

He clamped his sombrerote back on his head. Then he looked over at me with a defiant expression as though challenging me to smile back at him in derision.

After that we walked over to Ciudad Juárez to eat fritanga and drink a Chiquita Chihuahua together.

María Tepache

Amado Muro

In San Antonio, I got off a Southern Pacific freight train near the tracks that spidered out from the roundhouse turntable. When I quit the train it was almost five o'clock, and the sky was dark with the smoky pall of thunderheads. I was tired and chilled and hungry. I hoped to find something to eat and then get on to Houston.

Nearby was a small white-frame Mexican grocery with a corrugated tin porch held up by a few warped scantlings. The window displayed lettuce heads and coffee in paper sacks, and near the door was a wire bin of oranges. A dog lay on the porch before the door. I went in and asked a buxom, gray-haired woman with a round face and untroubled eyes if she could spare some day-olds.

"Ay, Señora Madre de San Juan, I just fed four hoboes and I can't feed no more," she said.

I started out the door then, but she called me back. She stared at me, her dark eyes becoming very round. "Hijole, paisanito, what spider has stung you—you look sad and burdened like the woodcutter's burro," she said. "Well, I don't blame you. When bread becomes scarce so do smiles."

The gray-haired woman wore a blue dress that was cut straight and came to her knees, and she had on huaraches. She told me her name was María Rodriguez, but she said people all called her María Tepache because she liked tepache with big pineapple chunks in it so well. We talked of different things—about where she came from was one. She came from a Durango village populated mostly, she said, by old men, old women, and goats.

"I was born in one of those homes where burros sleep with Christians," she said. "I can read and eat with a spoon, but I'm not one of those women meant to live in homes that would be like cathedrals if they had bells. In our adobe hut village, we lived a primitive life with no more light than the sky gives and no more water than that of the river. But my father never stopped feeding me because he couldn't give me bonbons or clothing me because he couldn't dress me in silks."

She asked me where I was from, her face intent with strong interest. When I told her, she appeared surprised. "¡Válgame San Crispín! I'd never have guessed it," she said.

When I asked why, she smiled and said: "Most Chihuahua people don't talk so fast as we of Durango. But you talk fast, and with the accent of Santa María de todo el mundo."

After that she put on a cambaye apron with a big bow in back, and led me to the back of the store where all the living was done. "This is your humble kitchen—come in," she invited.

The place was like all the homes of poor Mexicans that I'd seen in Texas. There was a broken-legged woodstove, a shuck-tick bed, a straight-back chair, a mirror with the quicksilver gone, and a table covered with oilcloth frayed and dark at the edegs. Beyond the stove and to one side was an old cupboard with the doors standing open. The kitchen's bare floor was clean, and the walls were painted wood with only a calendar picture of Nicolás Bravo that hung crookedly from its nail as decoration. On a tiny shelf in a corner was a gilt-framed picture of María Guadalupana and a crucified Christ.

The window had burlap curtains, and Doña María explained why she put them up long ago. "In a place where there aren't any curtains on the windows you can't expect children to turn out well," she said.

She lit a coal-oil lamp, and set it on the table. Outside it was beginning to rain. Wind blew the rain in through the window and made the lamp burn unevenly and smoke the chimney. The chimney blackened until only a ring around the base gave off light. Doña María closed the window and afterward stood near the lamp and told me she was a widow. Standing there very still with heavy lashes lowered, she spoke of her husband and her voice was husky. The dog that had lain on the porch was curled on the floor by the bed, his head resting on his outspread paws and his eyes watching her.

"In our village my husband was an adobero, and he

came here to earn dólarotes in the pecan mills," she said.
"I wasn't one of those model Mexican wives who leave
their wills in the church, but we were happy together and I
never worried that he'd fall in love with another chan-
cluda prettier than me. He couldn't read or write, but I
went through the fourth grade at the Justo Sierra School
and I taught him about numbers so he could count the
stars with our first son. When our centavos married and
multiplied, he talked about going back to Mexico. '¡Ay
Mariquita! If we can go back someday I swear I'll climb
Popocatepetl on my hands,' he told me. 'We could go to
Puebla on the other side of the volcanoes, and buy land
near the magueyes and milpas. We'll buy three cows, and
each will give her three litros. Our chilpayates will never
dance the Jarabe Moreliano with hunger.' "

Her eyes softened in a reflection of faraway dreaminess.
She said her husband made Puebla sound like Bagdad, and
talked of singing to her with twenty mariachis.

"Now I live with no more company than my own sins,"
she said. "I pass my life tending the store, and mending
the clothes of my many grandchildren." She broke off and
lowered her lids over her eyes, veiling them. Her mouth
grew set, a thin, straight line; she passed her hands over
her forehead as though awakening from sleep. Her gray
hair was in a tangled cloud about her face, and she looked
older than I'd thought at first seeing her. But when she
looked up toward me, she was smiling again and her dark
eyes were calm and reflective. "My grandchildren are less
brutes than I," she said. "All of them know how to speak
the gringo."

I hung my crumpled crush hat on a nail behind the kitchen
door and went out in the backyard to split stovewood. The
backyard was cluttered with piled-up packing boxes and
crates, and the grass was yellow with sand. There was a
stumpy cottonwood near the water tap, and a row of sweet-
peas clinging to a network of strings tacked on the fence.
The cottonwood leaves had turned yellow, but they were
still flat with green streaks showing in them. Every once
in a while the wind would shake the branches and a flurry
of dry leaves and dust funneled up near me.

I split wood, carried out ash buckets, and brought
water in a zinc pail. While I worked, Doña María bent over
a larded frying pan and told me about her father.

"He was a shepherd and a good man—never ambitious

for the centavos," she said. "He was happy and contented with no more ambition than not to lose a lamb and go down to Santiago Papasquiaro two or three times a year to hear the mariachis play in the plaza and listen to the church bells."

When I finished the chores, night was coming and the rain was heavier. There was lightning, vivid flashes that scarred the sky, and I could see San Antonio's lights golden as oil lamps beyond the New Braunfels Bridge. The rain fell through the yellow lamplight streaming from the kitchen window and cars, their lamps wet gems, moved slowly across the high bridge. Their headlights seemed to draw the raindrops, like moths. I looked at them for a moment, rain spattering off my shoulders, then went inside.

Doña María had finished setting the table. She wiped sweat from her forehead wtih a fold of her apron, and began to fan herself. Then she motioned me to a plate filled with refried beans, rice, and blanquillos.

"Esa es mecha," she said. "It will make you feel like shouting, 'Yo soy Mexicano,' in the middle of a crowded street. Eat—one can think of nothing good when he's hungry."

I ate so fast I grew short of breath. Doña María watched me with her arms wrapped in her apron and crossed over her chest. She looked solemn except for a faint flicker of a smile at the corner of her mouth. The dog sat on his haunches beside her bare legs.

When I finished, she gave me an ixtle shopping bag filled with tamales de dulce, nopalitos, a milk bottle of champurrado, and a tambache of flour tortillas wrapped in a piece of newspaper. I tried half-heartedly to refuse it. But she insisted I take it.

"I have enough for today, perhaps tomorrow, and another day too," she said. "After that, God will say."

When I thanked her, she smiled her mild smile and told me to say the prayer of San Luisito every day.

"May the Indian Virgin who spoke with Juan Diego protect you and cover you with her mantle," she said when I went out the door, "and may you become rich enough to drink chocolate made with milk and eat gorditas fried in Guadalajara butter."

Perla Is a Pig

"Zeta"

PART I

He was an old man who peddled corn in the Mexican *barrio* and he had gone five days now without a sale because the rumor had spread that he urinated in his cornfield.

On the evening of this fifth day he slowly pushed his orange cart to the pig's pen to dispose of the freshly cut corn. Those which had become yellow, he fed to the black sow.

"It is the same, Perla," the old man whispered in his native Spanish. "Our misfortune is your joy. Or so it seems." The fat, black pig grunted as it crushed the tender corn ears. "So eat and grow fatter. We'll have you when you're ready."

He chuckled and playfully threw one of the ears at the pig. Then he rolled the cart behind the one room adobe shack and went to the water pump. He could see no one from there, for in the spring he had planted the tiny kernels of corn in circular furrows surrounding the shack, the pig's pen and his outhouse. Now it was summer and the green stalks were higher than a man's head.

He removed his eye-patch that hid a purple socket, which he rubbed as though he were scrubbing an elbow, to clean the phlegmy, white particles that caked there during the day. He washed only his face. He did not trouble to roll up his sleeves and so his cuffs were always brown and wrinkled, as were his other garments. He dried his face with his shirt tails, then with his hands still wet, he flattened his few thin strands of yellow hair.

He went into the outhouse to complete his toiletry. He laughed to himself of the new rumor as he urinated.

He took some corn and picked green squash growing alongside the plum tree next to the shack to prepare the meal for the guest he was expecting within the hour.

The corn had not yet cooked when the old man heard

his guest's whistle. "I'm in here, Nico. Come on in," he responded.

Nico, the business invitee, was about half the old man's size. He wore a Levi jacket, Levi pants, and Lama boots. His brilliant black hair was immaculate. He wore a long mustachio, as did the Mexican cowboys in Texas from whom he had learned all there was to know of manhood. This same little man had also learned from his mother that no gentleman should be out in the streets without a pencil, a pad of paper, a comb and, at the very least, fifty cents on his person.

He entered and said, "Ah, here you are, eh? I thought you might be out pissing." He giggled the shrill laugh of a dirty boy.

"Excuse my bad manners, but I'm at the stove now," the old man explained. "Sit down, Nico. Take all that weight off your feet."

Nicolas hung his nose over the boiling pots. "No meat, Huero?" he asked the old man whom they called *el Huero,* because of his light skin, green eye and yellow hair.

"Sorry, but she's not ready yet."

"Ah, what luck. When my mother told me you said it was urgent, I thought, or at least I had hoped that you were ready to stick the knife in its throat."

"In her neck," the old man corrected.

"In its neck, in its throat, what does it matter? So long as we can get to it. I saw it when I came in. He's going to be beautiful, he'll bring in a lot."

"She is beautiful, Nico . . . Why don't you sit down?"

"Can I help?"

"No, just rest yourself."

"I thought you might want me to help set the table. I don't mind, Huero. Shall I get the wine glasses?"

"No, we won't need them. I thought we might drink some goats' milk. It's nice and fresh," the old man said, smiling.

"Goats' milk? Yes, it's nice. My mother serves it every night. Says it's supposed to be good for your liver."

"I know, you've told me. That's why I thought you might like it."

The little cowboy waited a moment. "I wouldn't mind trying some of your wine though, Huero," he suggested.

"Wine? But, Nico, what would your mother say? She'd smell it, you know."

"That is of no consequence, Huero! . . . besides, I can stop at Lodi's and get some sweets on the way home."

The old man turned and faced Nicolas. "Well, if you want. But don't tell the old lady. She's mad at me as it is. Like all the others, she wouldn't buy my corn today because of this new rumor. It's up to you."

"Jesus, hombre! I'm fifty-five! You think I worry about her?"

"Well, I don't know, Nico. She's what? Seventy-five?"

"I don't know. I suppose."

"I don't mind, Nico. You're the one living with her."

"So what? Come on, *viejo*, don't play games with me. . . . I have to stop at Lodi's anyway. She wants some of that Mexican chocolate."

The two men ate the meal and drank the wine. They did not speak of the business for which the cowboy had come. When they finished, they sat outside and watched the orange, purple sun silently disappear somewhere behind the brown foothills surrounding their valley of San Joaquin. They sat on huge logs smoking slowly. The mosquitoes from the cornfield picked at the little cowboy. He constantly swung at them and cursed them. Huero, the older man, made no such motions. Even if one were to rest on his eyeless socket, he did not bother it.

"Well, Nico, we'd better start on the business," the old man said suddenly, throwing the cigarette at the water pump.

"Business! What business?" Nicolas asked with surprise.

"Don't come at me with foolishness, Nico. You know it well."

"If you have some, well go ahead, but I don't know what you have in mind," the little cowboy said innocently.

"Then why are you here?" Huero said impatiently. "Are you here only to eat and drink?"

"My mother only said you wanted me for dinner as a guest."

"Guest? Ah, what a guest! . . . You know, Nico, sometimes you are like a pimp."

"A pimp? A pimp! Huero, you slander me."

"Quiet yourself, I say it without malice. What I mean is, you try to hide your business, your true business, I mean."

"Business? That I am a pimp? You know, Huero, sometimes I seriously believe you're losing it. Maybe what they said was true . . . maybe you did lose your eye from syphilis."

"Don't start, Nico."

"Well, I don't know, Huero. How should I know? How does anyone know anything?"

"Let it alone, *viejo!*" the old man of one eye warned.

But the little cowboy would not let it alone. "God only knows, *viejo*, but I should know. I who am your friend. Your counselor. Your business agent. Of a truth, if anyone should know, if anyone should know how you lost your eye, it should be me. But you are stubborn, you don't know who your true friends are."

"Look, Nico, we haven't time for that. This new rumor is serious. I've not sold one *helote* all week."

"But it might be important to this case," Nicolas reasoned. "Perhaps the original rumor has not died down. Perhaps it is a recurrence of the same thing."

"It is not the same thing, you jackass! I tell you this is new gossip, a new rumor. Forget the others. I tell you I've not sold all week. You know corn must be sold within a day or two lest it rot."

"Huero, you are using too many vile names. I cannot concentrate when you are rude to me."

"He's gone and started another one on me, Nico. I know it is he. And you know the children need their corn."

"Who?"

"*Ay*, but look at what a mosquito you are! Who? Who else but the fat Spaniard, you runt!"

"Lodi? Lodi Ulloa?"

"And he's using the same tricks. He has no morals, that *español!* To use one's children to spread evil gossip shows poor education. To gain a business advantage one should not have to lie. He is poorly educated, that one is."

"Huero, if you have something to tell me, why do you hide it? I know nothing of any rumor. I know only of the ones I helped you with in the past."

"But why do you play the part of the cat with this mouse? If indeed you do not know, then why did you ask me if I was pissing in the cornfield when you first entered?"

"Well, that is a natural thing, Huero. Surely you know that."

"You think I don't know what you're doing? You think I am such a fool?" The old man brought out another cigarette. He lit it carefully, deliberately. He inhaled evenly and waited for the words to come to him; for now the bargaining had begun. His words came firmly: "So you know nothing of this new rumor, is that it, Nico? You have no knowledge of the pissing in the cornfield, of the condition of sales. You are here only as a guest."

The counselor cowboy arose and stepped on the stub of his cigarette with the heel of his boot. "*Viejo*, I'm merely here sitting, smoking, and listening to the talk of a man who it seems to me has a problem, and who is talking like a mad one . . . A man, I should remind you, who claims to be a *Mejicano*, though he has blond hair and one green eye."

"*Ay, dios*, save me from this imbecile! I tell you we have work to do, we have plans to make, arrangements and terms of the agreement to decide . . . And if my color is different from the others, of what concern is that now?"

Nicolas scratched his ear. "How should I know? I remember some years back there was talk you were a gringo."

The old man did not speak now. He saw Nicolas pull at his ear with his thumb and forefinger. He watched him as he stared at the ground and occasionally at the sky which was now black and dotted with pin points of white and orange.

Nicolas paced the ground before the old man. Now and then he would stop and look directly into the old man's face. Now that the counselor cowboy was at work, the old man did not interfere. "Shall I tell you the details?" Nicolas finally asked.

"You know you have charge in the matter."

"With the thing about your being a gringo . . . sst! Nothing. A word here, a suggestion in the right ear . . . nothing! A child could have thought that one . . . That was the first rumor, no?"

"As I recall. And this is harder?"

"A gringo! Eh, it was so simple I've forgotten how I did it."

"You made me paint the Mexican flag on the cart."

"Ah, *sí*. A flag . . . sst! A child could have done that one." The cowboy pulled up his slight shoulders. "But you shouldn't have taken it off. Who knows, if you had left it on, and it wasn't that bad looking, maybe you wouldn't be facing this now."

"It looked like a child's drawing," the old man said simply.

"What's that to you. It served its purpose. They thought you were a gringo, because of your color. They would not let you drink in peace at the cantina . . ."

"And so you had me paint a flag on my peddler's cart to prove I am a *Mejicano*."

"Yes, if that's what it took, why not? They no longer bother you at the cantina with their questions, do they? I don't know, Huero, you bring these things on yourself."

"That's of no consequence now, Nico. Let's get on with it."

"No? But that's your problem. You concern yourself only with your own ways, with the things of today. You are like a mule, each day you must learn what you were taught the day before. You do not see the continuity of things."

"Don't start again, Nico," the old man pleaded.

"No, you are stubborn! You surround yourself too much with yourself thinking that by so doing you are hiding from others. But you are only calling attention to yourself."

"How's that?"

Nicolas stopped his pacing. Looking down at the corn peddler like a judge from his bench, he said, "Like this corn. Look at it!" He pointed to the circular furrows.

"What's that matter?"

"Well, look. *Jesús y María,* what a man you are! Who ever heard of a round field?"

"It helps the land. It rotates the soil, Nico."

"What a help! Don't you come at me with this foolishness. I know why you did this. And as you can see, everyone else knows."

"What? How's that?"

"To help the land! What nonsense. Who ever saw a round field of corn? It is clear to me, Huero. You did it to hide them. Do you think we are such fools? Even to the children it is clear."

"Hide? But what have I to hide?"

"Well, what else but the pig. And perhaps your plums. There is nothing else. Unless it was to hide your laziness. So that you could piss outside your house without being detected."

"I hide nothing, you *idiota!*" Huero exclaimed.

"But look at yourself. I try to help you. I give you counsel. You do well with my instructions at the beginning, but then as soon as you are doing well then you refuse to abide by my directions. Either you forget or you are a fool.

When will you learn?" The cowboy shook his head and sucked at his teeth.

"I should have left that flag painted on my cart? What for? They took that, a child's drawing, as evidence of my *raza*? Anyway, I choose not to go to the cantina anymore."

"Yes, and now you come to me for help again."

"Yes, but I know that I will not always need the counsel of a spider. God will forgive me this weakness . . . but as I have said, this is a different matter."

"That is where you are a fool or a child. Can you not see it? Are you really such a *pendejo*?"

The old man pondered. "You really think this is the same thing?"

"It is for the same reasons," Nicolas said, tossing an obvious rule of law to the wind.

Huero tugged at the cigarette and nodded at the sky. He inhaled the warm breeze and fixed his gaze on Venus. "And the syphilis? That came after the gringo thing. Was that also part of it?"

Now the little cowboy from Texas was in his glory. "Exactly. Look . . . First it was the gringo. They would not give you the drinks, right? So you painted a flag. It was a simple idea, true, but it was good, and it worked . . . Then you removed it. And then what happened? Then they started the rumor of the syphilis; that you lost your eye because of syphilis."

"Well, it wasn't clear. It was sin, I think."

"Sin, syphilis, they are one and the same."

The teacher continued without interest in the obvious past. "Look, dumb one. Pay attention. Sin, syphilis, what does it matter what they think. The reason behind the acceptance of a rumor hardly matters. What matters is that you cure them."

"I went to church as you suggested."

"Yes, you went to the mass . . . One time."

"I couldn't do it, Nico. I went the one time to show them where my religious thoughts were. I didn't mind that one time to prove to them, but to continue . . . Besides, the padre was a gringo, an Italian, they say."

"Sometimes I think you do have syphilis, Huero. It has spoiled your brain like a squash that has rotted from the frost. . . . Can't you see it was not for religion that I sent you there? It was to dispel the suggestion of sin."

"You believe that, Nicholas?"

"No, of course not. I am merely a counselor giving argument."

"I can't see it," the old man said, scratching his socket.

"Sure, look, it is very simple. If you had continued to go, if you had gone but a month and waited for the padre to hear of your sins. If you would have had the padre bless you in front of all the people . . . sst! You think Lodi would have dared start another rumor after that? Not even an español would be so stupid!"

The old man laughed fully. He slapped the ground and nodded slowly, saying, "*Ay, que cabrón,* what a bastard you are! You have such crazy notions."

"It is not a thing to laugh at. You refused to carry out my instruction, you refused to go get blessed and so now what? Now you have to wear that patch over your eye, that is what. But that is not all, and this is what you still do not see . . . This thing of the pissing is the same thing."

"I guess I'm too old."

"Then listen . . . You've worn that patch for three years now. And the people have forgotten about the syphilis. But the patch was your idea, it was certainly not one of mine. I am like a surgeon. I cut away the roots. With that patch you merely delayed this new one. You merely hid the sin. Now Lodi has seen fit to start another one because you have been selling too well in the past few years . . . so there you have it. Listen to my counsel and you will be cured once and for all."

The crickets lessened their clicking and the frogs took up their place. Mosquitoes hummed and buzzed while the fireflies occasionally bit the night air. Now there was a suggestion of a moon, as the Mexican cowboy issued his judgment. The counselor paced before the old man. He smoked and sighed now and again. "I have it! I have found it!" Nicolas burst suddenly. "Ho, ho, there we have it, *viejo!*" He shouted to the old man.

"Has the wine gone to your head, Nico?" asked the old man, thinking that perhaps Nicolas was drunk.

"Si, Nico! Nicolas Bordona! Old Nico has done it again. Go and get us some wine, old man," the cowboy ordered.

"Sit down and tell me. Calm yourself before your heart falls to your feet," said the old man.

"No, give me some wine first!" Nicolas paraded before the peddler, like a proud bantam rooster after the battle.

"Bah! who has need of wine when his head is full like mine?"

"Have you a good plan, a big one?" asked the old man.

"Good? You say *good? Ay, ay, ay!* Don't use such small words."

"Well, tell me. What clown do I play this time, doctor?"

"Sst! Clown? I'm not a beginner anymore, old man. My ideas have grown with me. I remember before I used to need the quiet of my home, a certain solitude, before they came to me . . . Clown? No more."

"Well hurry and say it, Nico," the old man was impatient with the cowboy's crowing.

"Yes, I'm growing big in my old age. You should see what ideas I have. Before, the thing of the flag, of the church, they were nothing. Sst! *Nada,* not a thing. A child, an idiot could have worked those up. But this one? I'm telling you, Huero, right from up there."

"You're telling me nothing, Nico."

"Nothing, I tell you," he continued without paying heed to the old man. "In those earlier years it was nothing . . ."

"For the love of God, Nico, say it and be done with it!"

With that the counselor returned to earth from his exaltation and began to unfold his plan before the peddler of corn who had gone five days without a sale because of the rumor in the Mexican *barrio* that said he urinated in his round cornfield. "Here you have it," began the cowboy. "This plan must dispel, once and for all, all the bad feelings of these people, these Mexicans of superstition. This plan must wipe out from their minds the idea that you are different, or that you are unclean. These are the things that tell the people that you are not one of us, and it is for these reasons that they accept the rumors about you. It is a universal occurrence that people will believe what they want to believe according to their feelings of the person in question; and these people, perhaps because they are but poor Mexicans, these people will believe any malicious gossip about you until you can show them . . ."

The old man interrupted, "Nico, please. I have no need for speeches."

"Oh? Then you do not want the basis, the reasoning behind the plan, is that it?"

"Just tell me what I must do, *por favor*."

"I see. Here I will show you . . . You see, the people, including the children, they believe you have planted your round rows of corn to hide something. To hide what? you may ask. Well, that I do not know, but again you stand apart, again you show your difference and thus again you give them cause for suspicion. Maybe they think you have something special, your pig, your plums, who knows? But I do know that it is because of that that they find it so easy to accept the accusation of this pissing."

"Nico! Jesus, hombre, speak! Say something!"

"Yes, yes. You are without learning. You have no love of philosophy in you."

"It is not philosophy I seek from you, worm. Nor these devious words of yours. I only want to know what I must do to sell my corn. Now will you counsel me or shall I seek out another?"

The counselor sighed deeply and shook his head more in pity than in disgust at the old man of such little knowledge, and then he said, "You will give your plums to the children."

"Give my plums?"

"Yes. To get them, and this is why I like this plan, to get them to spread, as it were, a rumor come from you. In a word, to get them on your side."

The old man turned his one eye up toward the little cowboy. *Surely the wine has gone to this one's head,* the old man thought. *For I ask him to sell my corn and he tells me to give away my plums.*

The gnarled, black-trunked tree blossomed violet each Spring and when the sun assaulted the hot fields in July the boys from the *barrio* crept through the tall green, yellow stalks and stole away the old man's plums. He knew of their entrance, he saw them run through the field, their pockets laden with the purple fruit. He heard them giggle their fear away, but he never once in all those years prevented their taking, without asking, the gorgeous, tender fruit, sweet to the dry mouths of brown-baked Mexican boys.

"Give them my plums, eh? To get them on my side?"

"Yes, that is the first part. I will go and tell them that you have decided to give away your plums. Then, and this is where the plan intrigues me. Then I will go and see Lodi and compliment him on his good meat."

"His meat?"

"Yes, his meat. I will tell him he has the best meat in the entire valley . . . And then, and then, ho, ho, ho . . . and then I will tell him that others have said the same thing."

The old man scratched at his eyeless socket. "That he has good meat, the best in the valley."

"Yes, and then . . . but this is good! Then I will, ever so slowly, suggest to him that if I were he I'd raise the price. *It is worth it, Lodi,* I shall say. *Not only is it the best, but it saves us a trip to Riverbank; and above all, we do not have to deal with the gringos.* I can do such a thing, you know, Huero. You know I have a way with words. *Si, Lodi, were it not for you we would have to buy from those fucking gringos.* And then, Huero, as you shall see, and then he will in fact raise the price of his meat. And it would not surprise me if he raises all his prices, for I will blow up his head 'til it is like a pumpkin, you'll see."

The old man nodded in amazement. He could barely speak. "I see, he'll raise the price of his meat, that's it?"

"Sure. And then all you have to do is sell yours for about ten cents cheaper."

The old man shook his face and scratched at his head. He spoke quietly, "Nico, I am not selling meat! I'm trying to sell my corn."

"Well, sell meat, dumb one."

"But it is you who are the dumb one. I have no meat to sell."

"And the pig?"

"Perla? She is not ready yet."

"Ready? Why not? The animal looks good and ready to me."

Huero looked toward the pig's pen. "Then I am not ready, frog!"

"We must truly come from different countries, Huero. I cannot understand how it is your head works. Here I've arrived at a solution, what appears to me to be the ultimate solution to your problem. A plan that will not only help you sell your pig and your corn but most important it will endear you to these people. For as even you can see, when the women learn from their sons that you are a generous man given to kindness, they will think well of you. When you tell the children that you planted the round field to keep away the dust from the roads to protect your beautiful animal so that she would be clean, how can they not think well of you? . . . And then when these same women learn that the *espanol,* that fat one who is not a *Mejicano,* when they hear that he has raised all his prices . . . Can't you see it? There you are, a kind man selling clean pork at

bargain prices on Sunday afternoon in front of the church
. . . Jesus, hombre, it is a beauty!"

"What? What's this of the church? And this thing about
the dust not getting on Perla, what is that? So again you
would have me play the clown and tell more lies. Again
you would have me fight one lie with another one."

"So what? What is that to you? Look, you fool, you'll
sell cheaper, true, but you'll sell it all in one day, or in
two at the most while the story circulates. It'll mean less
work and then next week you can go back to your corn.
By then that story will be dead . . . It is simple. You kill
the pig tomorrow. You give the boys the plums and tell
them the story. Sunday you take the pig to the church at
twelve noon. I'll leave as they're saying the last prayers and
when the women start coming out I'll tell them you're
selling Perla for much less than what Lodi sells for. You
watch, you'll sell all the pig before the sun has set."

The old man sat quietly. He looked to the moon. He
nodded his head slowly as the blood rose to his head. He
clenched his fists and shouted at the little Texan, "Jesus
Christ! I must be as dumb as my pig. Why do I ask you to
counsel me? Why must I always turn to the spiders and the
mosquitoes for assistance? . . . All I want to do is sell my
corn and be left in peace. If I don't sell it, the worms will
have it. It is too late to have it dried for cornmeal; I've
given it too much water for that. And even if the worms
don't get to it the sun will take up the sweetness . . . And
you will have me slaughter Perla when she is not ready
. . . God, but I am surely a fool!"

The old man was explaining these things for himself,
because he knew now that he had already committed himself
to the plan by simply having asked the little man to counsel
him. But he wanted, for a later time, to have this seeming
rebellion as a comfort. He knew this would be his only
outburst. Now he was but a soldier offering his distaste for
war, knowing all along he would concede to his general.

He arose and went into his shack. He soon returned with
two glasses full of wine. They drank slowly while the old
man finished the examination of his conscience.

When he spoke again his voice was soft and without
emotion. "I'll fix the pig and be at the church at noon. Take
some corn on your way out. It is still fresh, I cut it only
yesterday."

Nicolas had seen the old man like this before, so he did

not speak further on the matter. He took only an armful of the green *helotes*. His fee was all the corn he desired throughout the season.

PART II

The old man had begun the fires under two large tin tubs filled with water. He honed at a long knife with a stone he had found at the river, while his pig snorted and grunted unaware and oblivious.

The line of boys came noisily through the dense field of green, yellow, brown stalks of seven, eight, nine feet. They walked in single file, all barefooted and in shortsleeved shirts or in none at all. They wore patched pants or swimming trunks. All were brown like earth, all had black eyes or brown hair too long or too short. Fifteen Mexican boys coming for their plums. They ceased their hornet's nest buzzing as they carefully approached the old man.

One came forward. "Well, here we are . . ." He hesitated. "Uh, Huero?"

The old man continued to sharpen the knife. *"¿Sí muchachos? ¿Que es?"*

The brown boy looked at his own mud-caked feet. "Well, Nico, Nicolas Bordona, he said . . . He said we could have the, some plums."

"Oh, *sí, muchachos.*" The old man hesitated, for he was unaccustomed to dealing with the children. "Take them. There they are."

"They have asked me to speak for them," the boy said.

"No we didn't!" One of the boys standing in file broke away. "You said we should let you talk, but I want to say it for myself."

"Well, speak," the old man said.

"Senor Huero. We, I want to thank you for the plums . . . And I am sorry I told those lies about you. But I had to. My father says it is for my own good. He made me."

"You're one of the Ulloa boys?"

"Si, senor. But I didn't believe the story."

"It's all right. One has to obey his father. It is that way."

"I know. My mother said so too. But aren't you mad at me?"

"No, son. I am not angry with you. If a father tells his son to lie, then he must lie. Sometimes one must lie of necessity."

The boys murmured. "See?" one reminded the others.

"I said it too," the shortest one called in.

"Huero," another said, "Huero, I'm sorry I called you a
. . . *el ciego*. I was just kidding."

"Eh, what does it matter? I wish I were blind. For all the
good my one eye does me, I might as well be blind."

"You can see, can't you?"

"Some things. But if I were totally blind then the government would pay me. They give you money if you cannot
see anything."

"Huero?" Another one called in. "Huero, I stole a piece
of sugar cane once when you weren't looking."

"Ah, what's a piece of sugar cane?"

"Me, too, 'ere," the shortest one squealed. "Oh, no, it
was a tomato, I think."

The others laughed at him and the old man smiled.

"One time you gave me too much change," another said,
"and I kept it. I'm sorry."

Each one in his turn confessed his sin before the old man.
He laughed or smiled and tried to offer consolation. But he
was running out of absolutions. Although he had been
amongst these children for seven years this was the first
time they had come to him. The plan, the counselor's
scheme, kept twisting within him. He looked at his sow
and he saw the water giving up the steam. He ran his finger
along the knife's edge. He used his eyeless socket to advantage. When he did not want others to see him he turned
that void toward the speaker. When people told stories, or
made attempts at laughing matter he wished not to hear,
he would turn away from them. No one truly expected a
man with one eye to have all his wits, or to be completely
competent in his perception and therefore no one called
this rudeness to his attention.

So now as the boys looked upon him without their
accustomed rudeness, the scheme raced through him. He
turned away from them because he did not like to look
upon people when they could measure his emotion. He
looked at his plum tree and at his pig. He exhaled deeply,
resignedly and decisively. "Look, *muchachos,* did not Nico
tell you you could have the plums? Have I not said, take
them? Well, take them, they are yours . . . Not just now,
but whenever you want them. This year and the next. They
are yours. It will be your tree."

"Always?" one asked.

"Yes. It is yours . . . but there is just one condition.

You must do me just one favor in exchange . . . You must not tell anyone about this . . . You must keep this a secret between us. Not even the girls. Because, well . . . the more people know, the fewer plums it will be for you." He smiled and saw it was not so difficult to speak to them. He saw clearly that they were but little boys with dirty bare feet and that all he wanted was to peddle his corn.

"Huero, you say *always?* With your permission, may I ask, Are you going away?"

"Don't you like the plums, Huero?" another asked. "Do they make you sick? My mother says if you eat too many you'll get sick."

"No, I'm not going away. Not now, at least."

"But you are going away? You say not now?"

"Well, everyone goes away someday, you know."

The short one chirped in. "You mean to die? My dog died. My father said he was going away. I know he just died." This shortest one, a little bit of a boy, he was not the age of the others. He had merely come with his older brother to the feast.

"Boys, why don't you just take the plums."

"Are you very sick?"

"No, not very sick," the old man answered.

"My dog had a sickness. His eye was all red, and white, too. It was ugly. He had blood in it. Is that what you have, 'ero?" the little one asked.

The other boys turned to him and with their eyes and their faces they tried to warn him, to silence him. Their embarrassment compelled them to turn away from the old man with one eye.

"Well, in a way it is my eye, *hijo.*"

"Oh, I am sorry, 'ero. I'm very sorry you have the leprosy."

"Shut up, Paquito," his brother yelled.

"Why? I am sorry. And I know about it. The sisters told me about leprosy in catechism. It's like what Teto, my dog, that's what he had. He had it too. Isn't that what you have, 'ero?"

The old man chuckled. "I don't know, Paquito. Maybe I'll die of that, like your dog. His name was Teto, eh?"

"*Sí.* I called him that for my uncle Hector. And the sister said he just went away too. But I know he just died of the leprosy."

"I see. Well, look, boys, you've thanked me for the plums.

I say you are welcome. Now take them, they are yours. They are ripe now."

The boys did not wait. They leaped to the tree and pulled at the branches. The purple tender balls came off with a touch. They ate as they picked more to stuff in their pockets. They yelled and pushed and buzzed and filled their mouths with the fruit. It was not a big tree. Shortly it was clean of the fruit. With their mouths purple and their pockets wet, they left down the same path through which they had entered.

The old man stirred the flames more. "*Bueno*, Perla it is your time. I would have waited . . . but you have eaten well, have you not?"

What a pearl! he thought to himself as he drove the knife into her neck. He drained her blood, he sliced her skin, he burnt and scraped the bristles. He pulled the intestines. He preserved the brain and the eyes. He cut cleanly the meat from the fat.

Huero worked late into the night under a lamp beside the now thinned plum tree.

PART III

It was Sunday morning in the *barrio*. The old, wrinkled, burnt-skinned Mexican women, covered with black shawls, gathered at the entrance to the wooden building. The church steeple was crowned with a bleeding Christ and housed a hornets' nest.

The children in stiff bright clothes held back their laughter. They carried black or red or white missals. The men in tight, white starched collars and pin-striped black or brown suits smoked quickly before the mass began.

"Have you heard about the old man?" A woman asked several others.

The others came closer. "*Sí, que lástima,* what a pity."

"El Huero, you mean?"

"My boy told me. It is sad."

"I wonder if we shouldn't send the men to inquire."

"I don't know, we might be intruding. I don't want to be a *metichi*."

"Yes, but, Rosa, when it is a thing like this . . ."

"But with him? It is different. He does not join us."

"Well, it is a shame. But I could not buy his corn after what was said. My man would have thrown it to the trash."

"I know. It is the same with me. Mine would have

cracked a plate over my head . . . Still, he does have a
heart. Like my boy said—he's a little sick this morning,
I guess he ate too many . . ."

"Isn't that a coincidence? Manuelito is sick, too. You
say yours ate too many? What's that?"

"The plums. You know, Paquito said the old man gave
them some plums."

"Your boys are sick? You say Huero gave them . . ."

"Sí, Paquito said all the boys went there . . ."

"All the boys. Elisa, what are you saying? Don't you
know, didn't your boy tell you? My boy, Oscar, he told me
that Huero had some bad illness. He's sick too. He's got
stomach trouble."

"Wait a minute. Paquito . . . but he's just a baby, he
said the old man had what his dog died of. He said the
old man told him he was dying of leprosy. But surely, that
is just a baby talking."

"Leprosy!"

"Now wait, just wait. My boy, Oscar, he never lies, he
is a good honest boy; now he said, and he is no baby . . ."

"Well what is it, Rosa?"

"He did say the old man was sick, of a disease . . . You
say leprosy? But he said it might just be a rumor . . ."

"Jesús y María! If they all went there, as you say . . .
and he has leprosy . . . and now they are sick . . . Dios
mío!"

Several of them crossed themselves. Two of them, without another word, turned and ran home. The others talked
faster and louder and gathered momentum in their gesticu-
lations. They called the men into their discussions.

The men laughed at them and called them chirinoleras.
The men told their women to leave the old man alone. The
men in their tight clothes returned to finish their cigarettes,
for the priest had arrived.

The women continued in their anxiety. They quoted
scripture to one another. One suggested it was not com-
municable. Another said it was the mark of Cain. They
carried their grief into the church and prayed with the
priest for all the sick.

But it was all too late. For the rumor had spread during
the mass. During the collection, the rumor went round from
one to the other, from pew to pew, that the old man had
leprosy. The evidence was overwhelming, beyond a reason-
able doubt. The Huero had leprosy as was proven by the

illness of all the children who had eaten too many plums.

While the congregation recited their *Hail Marys*, the little cowboy slipped out to meet the old man who had rolled his cart near the entrance to the church.

"What's this about your illness?" The counselor wore a black suit and a green tie four inches wide.

"My illness? I am well."

"I don't get it all. I got here a little late. Mother wanted some fresh milk before I left. Look, here they come!" He spun around and hurried to the door to meet the women. But they would not stop to talk as was their custom. They only touched the priest's hand. They hurried away holding tightly to their children. They wanted to find a doctor. Some wanted to go to the older women, the very old and wiser women would counseled them in times of distress, the *viejitas* who found wild mint and red spinach among the peach trees for the illnesses of the children.

The women had no time for the politeness of the counselor who bid them seek out the old man's pork at bargain prices. Nicolas went from one to another pleading with them to look at the meat. They paid him no heed.

One of the women walked up to the old man standing by his cart, and the old man said, "*Ah, buenos días, señoras.* I have nice fresh meat, thirty cents to the pound. The skins are crisp and the blood is red."

"Huero, I don't come here to buy. I must know, this is a serious thing. Did my son, Paquito, did he go to your house yesterday?"

The old man arranged the meat in the cart of two unnecessarily large wheels, one painted black and the other white. The cart itself was painted orange. "Paquito? Well, what did he tell you?"

"That doesn't matter, Huero. He is just a boy. But I must know for certain. Did he?"

"Don't ask me. I know nothing of your son."

Nicolas came to his defense. "Ladies, perhaps what you should do is buy some of these *chicharrones* for your children. You know how they like them."

"You stay out of this, Nicolas Bordona. This is very serious. We have to know. Huero, we know you are sick and we know some of the boys went to your house yesterday. We have to know which ones."

"I am sick? What is this of my being sick?" he asked the

excited women who eyed the pork meat with the eye of the bargain hunter.

"*Sí, viejo,* we know of it. It is out and we've got to know which boys were exposed. Now tell us!"

"Señor Huero, please, this is a serious thing. Even though the *padrecito* just told me it is not catching, still we should know. I'm sorry if she is rude, but we are all concerned," a younger one apologized.

"I'm not being rude, Carmen. But leprosy is a bad thing, don't you know?"

"Leprosy?" the old man asked. "I have leprosy?"

They all fixed their gaze upon him. "Well, do you deny it?"

The old man touched his eye patch. "Where did you hear that one?"

"From the . . . the boys told us. I think it was Rosa's boy, Paquito, and Elisa's boy, Oscar, he said you told them."

The old man smiled and remembered. He looked at the meat in the cart and he remembered the confessions he had heard the previous day. He saw again the boys scampering through the plum tree and he chuckled when he thought of Paquito's dog, Teto. With a twinkle in his eye he said, "I don't know, ladies. How would I know what I have. I have not talked to a doctor since I was but a child. How should I know for certain if I have leprosy . . . for that matter who can say he does not have it."

The women stared at him and looked with nervous eyes at one another. They tightened their shawls about them and some clutched at the missal or rosary they held in their hands.

"Well, we know, at least the father told Carmen that it is not catching . . . But you are right, who knows."

"Maybe it's just a coincidence that they're all sick," Carmen said.

"Or a warning," Rosa said as she hurried away.

Nicolas said, "But ladies, how about this beautiful meat?"

"The meat? . . . No, I think I'll wait."

"But it's fresh, and it is much less than at Lodi's," he wailed.

"No, Nico . . . I don't think my man would want me to buy just now. Maybe we'd better wait until tomorrow, after we see a doctor or talk to the *viejitas,* they should know."

Nicolas tried the last remaining worshippers. But their decision was the same. They would wait until the following day. If their sons were only sick from too many plums . . . perhaps they would reconsider.

So now I am a leper, the old man chuckled to himself as he covered the meat in the cart with a white cloth.

"How do you do it, Huero? Of all my clients how is it that you bring me the most hardships?"

"It is over with, Nico."

"But you can bring me some problems, can't you? You cannot keep my counsel. You must always play the part of the clown."

"Leave it be, Nico. It is done."

"No, wait, *viejo*. This was a business matter. You were to take my advice for a price."

"You can have your corn, hyena. You can have all that enormous belly of yours will hold. But away with you and your advice!"

"I don't know, Huero. First a gringo, then syphilis, then the pissing . . . Now leprosy . . . But why did you not deny it? Why did you let them know that is what it is. Are you such a *pendejo?*"

"What are you saying, frog face?"

"Ah, well, never you mind, old man. I'll come up with another plan. You'll see. We'll sell your pig yet."

"Pig? But it is you who are the *pendejo*. This is not a pig. This is but pork meat, can't you see that? . . . Perla is a pig!"

For the first time the counselor took notice of the old man's seriousness. The little cowboy's eyes fluttered and he bit at his mustachio. "Huero, you are disappointed because the plan did not work. But then you should not have said anything about this leprosy. You should have denied it. You should not have let them know you have it, or whatever it is . . . So that is what it is. I thought, for years I had known you'd lost that eye from something strange and mysterious."

Huero pushed his cart away. The counselor followed after him and tried to stop him. The old man pushed his hand away angrily. He mumbled curses at the cowboy. Nico placed himself in front of the cart.

"Jesus, hombre, but you are loco. *Cabron,* but you are weak in the head," Nico shouted.

"Loco? Yes, Nico, that I am. I am weak in the head.

But as it goes, *He who has no head had better have good feet*. So get away from me before I run over you!"

Nicolas stepped away from the cart. "Jesus, but now you are like a wild one caged too long without water."

The old man advanced toward the little cowboy from Texas. "Nico, you know they say if a leper rubs his sore on sweet skin it will harden and fall off like cold wax. Want me to try it on you?"

Nicolas jumped back. "God, but now you've really gone off."

Huero laughed fully. His whole body trembled with delight as he watched the frightened little man scampering away with short steps like a busy field mouse.

The old man returned to his hut surrounded by circular furrows of tall corn stalks. He had planted it that way because he had read in a magazine that it did the soil good.

The Mexican peddler of corn hummed an old song as he dug a grave behind the plum tree. The grave was large enough for the coffin, which was the cart, stuffed with the meat of the pig that had once been his Perla.

He knew then, that he too, like Paquito's dog, would have to leave the Mexican *barrio* of Riverbank.

Retrato de un Bato Loco

Marcus Duran

"You know, ese, like I gotta have that geeze today. Like I've gotta kick cold turkey at that place called El Proyecto Del Barrio. I'm hurtin', ese. I'll pay you some other time."

The Horse stood blinking under the morning sun. He was decked out in ragtag khaki pants that had seen better days. He stood there knowing he had to feed a line of bullshit to the Dude for the half gram of stuff, otherwise he'd have to go out of the Barrio and hustle some loot, and that was a drag especially because of the way he was feeling at that precise moment. He was really hurting for a quick fix of junk.

"Orale, ese," he kept on, "come on, man, just this one time. My P. O. tells me either I go over the Proyecto, ese, and straighten, or like it's back to the joint. And I mean the big house on 'Frisco Bay. An' that ain't what I'm gonna do, ese, so before I split I need one last fix on credit. So how 'bout it, Carnal? Just one. I'll get the bread. I'll pay."

The Dude was one cool Chicano. He was cold, cold when it came to money. He had carga all right—he had it inside his mouth. He was loaded, and as he looked at the Horse his eyes were glazed and dilated. The Dude didn't answer right away. Sitting there in front of his clapboard shack, nodding, he was barely aware of the Horse's voice. He was thinking instead about the boss brown junk he'd brewed just that morning. It had dropped him against his bed when he'd jolted it into his scarred vein. He smiled. Good junk.

The stuff had come into his possession late last night. It was the kind of Chicano stuff that came in once in a great while, the kind you paid four C-notes for just a piece. The cut with sugar milk went four to one ounce, and it was really the best kind of junk. One ounce procaine made it five ounces. Twelve C-notes of Chicano junk. That was big time money. The Dude was happy. Business was going to pick up all right this week.

He looked up at Horse and squinted. *Yeah. He could afford to go along with the play and help the Horse out. A half gram. Anyhow, even though the Horse was splitting he'd pay sometime. Sometimes a little credit was good for business anyway. Beside, he sorta liked the Bato.*

"Ese, Caballo," the Dude said as he swatted away a fly buzzing around his head, "tell you what. I'm gonna give you a good taste, man. Like I dig the scene you've gotta make." He dropped a small piece into the Horse's trembling hand. "It's solid carga, man, so don't do it all up at once. Now, get outta here, man, you're putting heat on my pad. See you later when everything gets cool with you."

The Horse mumbled something, dropped the carga into his mouth, and ran tumblingly along the path leading to the Barrio street. As he turned the corner of a building he ran headlong into one of the Bato Locos from the Barrio. It was Benny.

"Orale, ese," Benny said, stopping him.

The Horse eyed the Bato and he knew Benny was out to hustle some cotton. His eyes were watery and Horse could tell he was one sick Bato.

"You gonna score from the Dude, ese?" Horse said as he started to pass Benny by, but Benny held onto his arm.

"Yeah," Benny said, hanging on. "You get some, ese?" Benny was out to hustle, if he could.

"Yeah," Horse said, releasing Benny's hold gently. I got some from the Dude, ese. But not enough. I mean, I told him I had to split the scene or they're gonna send me to Q. He gave me some, ese, on credit, but not enough."

"The Batos say you gotta dry out, ese. You supposed to be goin' over to the Proyecto." Benny's brown eyes and clear brown skin reminded Horse of the leaves on the Oak tree in the Dude's yard.

"Naw, ese," Horse answered, irritated. "I ain't going on over to that Proyecto. I ain't gonna kick cold turkey for no motherfucker. My P. O. and all them lame putos can go fuck themselves. They ain't gonna get on me. I'm heading home, ese and do me in this carga I got; then I'm splitting."

Benny stared at him. "Yeah, ese, fuck it. Well, man, I've got to make the scene. Later, ese, Caballo."

"Later, Benny."

The Horse made it trotting to his pad and tiptoed inside the shabby living room. His grandmother wasn't around and he breathed a sigh of relief. She was always bugging him about fixing around the house. He quietly opened the door to the bathroom and went inside. His outfit was hidden behind the washbowl. He pulled out the bundle and un-rolled the dirty piece of rag. His hand was shaking and the bent spoon fell into the toilet bowl. Sweat was breaking out on his brow, and he could feel the first symptoms of withdrawal. He scooped out the spoon and made the preparations. He knew he was strung out, but it wasn't too bad yet. Anyway, there was no way out. He had to take that last geeze before he split from the Barrio and hid out. He knew he could get some chiva wherever he went. Everybody was hooked. The shit was everywhere, so he wasn't worrying about scoring. He sure as hell wasn't going to no Proyecto and let them cold turkey him, fuck it!

He broke the red balloon and spilled out the brown carga into the match-burn blackened spoon. Then he ripped off five matches from the paperbook that lay on the toilet seat. The needle and eyedropper were ready. He cooked the junk and felt his guts turning inside out, and he was already choking with the puke that came up to his throat. He put all of the carga into one good jolt.

The Horse pressed the nipple of the eyedropper and carefully withdrew the jet-black carga from the spoon. The rag was tight around his upper right arm where the muscle bulged with the pressure. The needle penetrated his flesh into the mainline vein and blood sucked back into the eyedropper. Everything was going right, for sure, that was for sure.

Then the Horse felt what he'd never felt before. It was a blinding flash, and he felt his knees buckling under him. He didn't know, couldn't know, what was happening, but he knew things were sweet, nauseatingly sweet, and his body flew in space, and all that was a part of him was sud-denly a part of the darkness that came after the flash, a darkness that disappeared a moment, making him briefly aware of his grandmother's piercing, haunting scream, the darkness wavered, and he gave himself up to the complete-ness of it.

On the Road to Texas:
Pete Fonseca

Tomas Rivera

He'd only just gotten there and he already wanted to leave. He arrived one Sunday afternoon walking from the little town where we bought our food Saturdays and where they didn't mind that we came in the afternoon all dirty from work. It was almost dark when we saw this shape crossing the field. We'd been fooling around in the trees and when we saw him we were almost scared, but then we remembered there was more of *us* so we weren't so scared. He spoke to us when he got near. He wanted to know if there was any work. We told him that there was and there wasn't. There was, but there wasn't till the weeds grew. It'd been pretty dry and the weeds didn't grow and all the fields were real clean. The boss was pretty happy about it since he didn't have to pay for weeding the onion fields. Our parents cursed the weather and prayed for rain so the weeds'd grow and we had to make like we cared too, but really we liked getting up late, wandering around in the trees and along the stream killing crows with our slingshots. That's why we said there was but there wasn't. There was work but not tomorrow.

"Aw, fuck it all."

We didn't mind him talking like that. I think we realized how good his words went with his body and clothes.

"There's no god damned work no fuckin' place. Hey, can you give me something to eat? I'm fuckin' hungry. Tomorrow I'm going to Illinois. There's work for sure . . ."

He took off his baseball cap and we saw that his hair was combed good with a pretty neat wave. He wore those pointed shoes, a little dirty, but you could tell they were expensive ones. And his pants were almost pachuco pants. He kept saying *chale* and also *nel* and *simón* and we finally decided that he was at least half pachuco. We went with him to our chicken coop. That's what we called it because it really was a turkey coop. The boss had bought ten little turkey coops from a guy who sold turkeys and brought them to his farm. We lived in them, though they were

[52]

pretty small for two families, but pretty sturdy. They didn't leak when it rained, but even though we cleaned them out pretty good inside they never really lost that stink of chicken shit.

His name was Pete Fonseca and Dad knew a friend of his pretty good. Dad said he was a big mouth since he was always talking about how he had fourteen gabardine shirts and that's why they called him *El Catorce Camisas*. They talked about fourteen shirts a while and when we went to eat beans with slices of Spam and hot flour-tortillas, Dad invited him to eat with us. He washed his face good and his hands too, and then he combed his hair real careful, asked us for Brilliantine and combed his hair again. He liked the supper a lot and we noticed that when Mom was there he didn't use pachuco words. After supper he talked a little more and then lay down on the grass, in the shadow where the light from the house wouldn't hit him. A little while later he got up and went to the outhouse and then he lay down again and fell asleep. Before we went to sleep I heard Mom say to Dad that she didn't trust that guy.

"Me neither. He's a real con man. Gotta be careful with him. I've heard about him. *Catorce Camisas* is a big mouth, but I think it's him who stabbed that wetback in Colorado and they kicked him out of there or he got away from the cops. I think it's him. He also likes to smoke marijuana. I think it's him. I'm not too sure . . ."

Next morning it was raining and when we looked out the window we saw that Pete had gotten in our car. He was sitting up but it looked like he was sleeping because he wasn't moving at all. I guess the rain waked him up and that's how come he got in the car. Around nine it stopped raining so we went out and told him to come have breakfast. Mom made him some eggs and then he asked if there was any empty house or some place he could live. And when was work going to start? And how much did they pay? And how much could you get a day? And how many of us worked? Dad told him that we all worked, all five of us, and that sometimes we got almost seventy bucks a day if we could work about fourteen hours. After breakfast Dad and Pete went out and we heard him ask Dad if there was any broads on the farm. Dad answered laughing that there was only one and she was sort of a loser. La Chata, snub-nose. And they went on talking along the path that went round the huts and to the water pump.

They called her La Chata because when she was little she got sick with something like mange on her face and the nose bone had got infected. Then she got better but her nose stayed small. She was real pretty except for her nose and everyone spoke bad about her. They said that even when she was little she liked men a lot and everything about them. When she was fifteen she had her first kid. Everyone blamed one of her uncles but she never told who it was. Her Mom and Dad didn't even get angry. They were pretty nice. Still are. After that, she'd shack up with one guy and then another and each one left her at least one kid. She gave some away, her parents took care of others, but the two oldest stayed with her. They were big enough to work now. When Pete arrived, it was just two weeks after she'd lost again: her last husband had left, he didn't even get mad at her or anything. Just left. La Chata lived in one of the biggest chicken coops with her two sons. That's why Dad told Pete there was only one and she was sort of a loser. We figured Pete was pretty interested in what Dad said, and it seemed pretty funny since La Chata must've been about thirty-five and Pete, well he couldn't be more than twenty-five.

Anyhow, it turned out he *was* interested in what Dad said because later, when we were fooling around near the pump, he asked us about La Chata. Where did she live, how old was she, was she any good? We were just talking about that when La Chata came down to get water and we told him that was her. We said hello to her and she said hello to us, but we noticed that she kept on looking at Pete. Like the people say, she gave him the eye. And even more when he asked her her name.

"Chavela."

"Hey, that's my mother's name."

"No kidding."

"Honest, and my grandmother's, too."

"You son-of-a-bitch."

"You don't know me yet."

La Chata left the pump and when she was pretty far away, Pete sighed and said real loud:

"Hey, mamasita, mamasota linda!"

So she could hear, he told us after. Because according to him broads like to be called that. From then on we noticed that everytime La Chata was near Pete he would always call her *mi chavelona* real loud. He said it loud so she'd hear and I think La Chata liked it because when work started she always chose the rows nearest Pete and if he got ahead of her she'd try and catch up. And then when the boss brought us water Pete always let her drink first. Or he helped her get on and off the truck. The first Saturday they paid us after Pete got there, he bought some fritos for La Chata's kids. That's how it began.

I liked it best when he sang her songs. Pete was going to stay and work, he'd say, until everything was over. He went to live with two other guys in an old trailer they had there. We used to go after supper to talk to them, and sometimes we'd sing. He'd go outside, turn towards La Chata's house and would sing with all his might. In the fields too we'd just get close to her or she'd come along and Pete would let go with one of his songs. Sometimes he even sang in English: *sha bum sha bum* or *lemi go, lemi go lober*, and then in Spanish: *Ella quiso quedarse, cuando vió mi tristeza . . . Cuando te hablen de amor y de ilusiones*. Sometimes he'd even stop working and stand up in the row, if the boss wasn't there, and he'd sort of move his hands and his body. La Chata'd look out of the corner of her eye, like it bothered her, but she always went on taking the rows next to Pete, or meeting him, or catching up to him. About two weeks later they both started going to get water at the truck together, when the boss didn't bring it, and then they'd go behind the truck a while and then La Chata would come out fixing her blouse.

Pete would tell us everything afterwards. One day he told us that if we wanted to see something we should hide behind the trailer that night and he'd try and get her to go in the trailer.

"You know what for . . . to give her some candy. . . ."

Us and the guys who lived with him hid behind the trailer that night and then after a long time we saw La Chata coming towards the trailer. Pete was waiting for her and she'd just got there and he took her hand and pulled her towards him. He put his hand up under her skirt and started kissing her. La Chata didn't say nothing. Then he leaned her up against the trailer, but she got away and told him you son-of-a-bitch, not so fast. Pete was inviting her to come into the trailer but she didn't want to and so they stayed outside. Do you love me, will you marry me, yes I will, when, right now, what about that other cat. Finally she left. We came out of the dark and he told us all about it. Then he started telling us all about other broads he'd made. Even white ones. He'd brought one from Chicago and set up his business in Austin. There, according to him, the bastards would line up at five bucks a throw. But he said that the broad he'd really loved was the first one he married the right way, in the Church. But she'd died with the first kid.

"I sure cried for that woman, and since then nothing. This fuckin' life . . . now with this *chavelona*, I'm beginning to feel something for her . . . she's a good person, if you know what I mean. . . ."

And sometimes he'd start thinking. Then he'd say real sincere like:

"Ay, mi chavelona . . . man, she's a hot one . . . but she won't let me . . . until I marry her, she says."

Three days after we'd hid, Pete decided to get married. That's why all that week that's all he talked about. He had nothing to lose. Why, him and La Chata and the two boys could save a lot. He'd also have someone to cook his gorditas for him and his nice hot coffee, and someone to wash his clothes and, according to Pete, she could handle at least one John a night. He'd start calculating: at four dollars a throw at least, times seven nights, that was twenty-eight dollars a week. Even if *he* couldn't work things'd be pretty good. He also said he liked La Chata's boys. They could buy a jalopy and then Sundays they could take rides, go to a show, go fishing or to the dump and collect copper wire to sell. In fact, he said, him marrying La Chavelona was good for all of them. And the sooner the better.

A little while later he came to talk to Dad one night. They went out on the road where no one could hear them and they talked a pretty long time. That night we heard what Dad and Mom were saying in the dark:

"Get this: he wants to marry La Chata! He wanted to elope with her, but what in? So it's better to get married for real. But—get this—he's got some sickness in his blood so he doesn't want to go into town and get the papers. So what he wants is for me to go and ask La Chata's father, Don Chon, for her hand. He wants me to go right away, tomorrow. . . . Don Chon, I've come today commissioned to ask you for the hand of your daughter, Isabel, in matrimony with young Pedro Fonseca . . . How's that, eh? . . . How's it sound, old lady? . . . Tomorrow after work, right before supper. . . ."

Next day all you heard about was how they were going to ask for La Chata's hand. That day Pete and Chavela didn't even talk to each other. Pete went around all day real quiet and sort of glum, like he wanted to show us how serious he was. He didn't even tell us any jokes like he always did. And La Chata also looked real serious. She didn't laugh any all day and every now and then she'd yell at her kids to work faster. Finally the work day finished and before supper Dad washed up, parted his hair four or five times, and went straight to Don Chon's house. Pete met him in the front yard and they both knocked at the door. They went in. *It was okay—they'd asked them to come in.* About half an hour later they all came out of the house laughing. *They'd agreed.* Pete was hugging La Chata real tight. Pretty soon they went into Chavela's house and when it got dark they closed the doors and pulled down the rags on the windows too. That night Dad told us about ten times what happened when he went to ask for her hand.

"Man, I just spoke real diplomatic and he couldn't say no . . ."

Next day it rained. It was Saturday and that was when we really celebrated the wedding. Almost everyone got drunk. There was a little dancing. Some guys got into fights but pretty soon everything calmed down.

They were real happy. There started to be more and more work. Pete, La Chata and the boys always had work. They bought a car. Sundays they'd go driving a lot. They went to Mason City to visit some of La Chata's relatives. She was sort of strutting around real proud. The boys were cleaner now than ever. Pete bought a lot of clothes and was also pretty clean. They worked together, they helped each other, they took real good care of each other, they even sang together in the fields. We all really liked to see them because sometimes they'd even kiss in the fields. They'd go up and down the rows holding hands . . . *Here come the young lovers.* Saturdays they'd go shopping, and go into some little bar and have a couple after buying the groceries. They'd come back to the farm and sometimes even go to a show at night. They really had it good.

"Who would of said that that son-of-a-gun would marry La Chata and do her so right? It looks like he really loves her a lot. Always calling her *mi chavelona.* And can you beat how much he loves those kids? I tell you he's got a good heart. But who was to say that he did. Boy, he looks like a real pachuco. He really loves her, and he doesn't act at all high and mighty. And she sure takes better care of him than that other guy she had before, don't you think? And the kids, all he does is play with them. They like him a lot too. And you gotta say this about him, he's a real hard worker. And La Chata too, she works just as hard. Boy, they're gonna pick up a pretty penny, no? . . . La Chata finally has it pretty good . . . Man, I don't know why you're so mistrusting, old lady. . . ."

Six weeks after the wedding the potato picking ended. There was only a couple of days more work. We figured Tuesday everything would be over and so we fixed up the car that weekend since our heads were already in Texas. Monday I remember we got up early and Dad like always beat us to the outhouse. But I don't even think he got there because he came right back with the news that Pete had left the farm.

"But what do you mean, old man?"

"Yeah, he left. He took the car and all the money they'd saved between him and La Chata and the boys. He left her without a cent. He took everything they'd made . . . What did I tell you? . . . He left . . . What did I tell you?"

La Chata didn't go to work that day. In the fields that's all people talked about. They told the boss about it but he just shook his head, they said. La Chata's folks were good and mad, but I guess we weren't too much. I guess because nothing had happened to us.

Next day work ended. We didn't see La Chata again that year. We came to Texas and a couple of months later, during Christmas, Dad talked to Don Chon who'd just come from Iowa. Dad asked about Pete and he said he didn't know, that he heard he'd been cut up in a bar in Minnesota and was going around saying the cops had taken all his money and the car, and that the boss had told the cops and they'd caught him in Albert Lea. Anyhow, no one had given any money to Don Chon or La Chata. All we remembered was how he'd only just gotten there and he already wanted to leave. Anyhow, Pete sure made his pile. But, like they say, no one knows who his boss is. That all happened around '48. I think La Chata must be dead by now, but her kids must be grown men.

Chavalo Encanicado

"El Chapo"

Mira Rafas, I start telling you about my cousin Tudi the last time I was in Los. Since I didn't finish the story, I'll just write you a short letter. I'll tell you how it was *en nuestros tiempos, ese*.

The cold lights of Los seen from my house in the barrio were not warm like my house and my family, *ese*. We always were taught to love life—in the way we laughed, in the way we danced, and in the way we enjoyed everything. But one kind of life we always had, more than any other kind, was chickens. ¡Hijo! Sometimes the other kids couldn't play tag in my yard for tripping on the chickens. Sure there was a dog, a goat, some rabbits, but always we had more chickens than anything.

Nicky Porras had a poultry shop, and every month I had to kill and pluck about thirty chickens for my mother who sold them to Nicky. Life was good for me then except for all them chickens. Those chickens almost messed up my love life for good, *ese*.

Rachel and Virgie were sisters, and man were they fine. They weren't really, but they looked like twins. They had eyes that were black and bright like the buttons on my mother's blue dress. Rachel always had little gold earrings that looked like crosses and Virgie always had ribbons in her hair. Red ribbons, blue ribbons, or green ribbons. And always the *vatos* would wait everyday to see what color ribbons Virgie would wear that day. It was a guessing game about Virgie's ribbons, and about if her older sister Cuca had already done it.

My cousin Tudi and me had tried to move on those chicks, but always it was the same. They couldn't go out, or the mother was sick, or they were going to their aunt's house in T.J. When I saw Rachel my heart would beat fast, and my mouth would get dry. My sister Lucía would call me *sinverguenza.* I guess Lucía was right. I was the roughest *vato* in the barrio, except maybe for Half-Man, and I was so *encanicado* with Rachel that it would hurt inside my heart when I saw her going to the store or hanging clothes in the back yard. Tudi dug on Virgie but it wasn't the same. *Era muy* cold-blooded *mi primo* Tudi.

One Saturday we was hunting doves out of season in San Fernando and me and Tudi were feeling all warm inside. The little bit of Red Mountain wine that old Alfredo had bought us was working good. Really fine. But the warm thing was not only in the wine. Warmness came too because me and Tudi had finally made a date with Rachel and Virgie, and man, we couldn't think of nothing else.

We couldn't go to their house to pick them up 'cause their old man didn't dig *vatos* scheming on his daughters. Me and Tudi didn't argue. Their father wasn't called "Big Bad Joe Garza" for nothing. I ain't no fool *ese*. Tudi neither.

We carried our .22's as we crossed the big field in San Fernando. We liked to go up there to hunt the doves. Man, it was a hot sun. But it was a good hot sun. "Someday," I thought, "I'm going to learn to whistle like that bird on the fence. That bird don't care that me and Tudi are walking toward him. He wants to sing, and he don't give a shit about no Mexicans with .22's."

We sat under a bush to rest. We listen to the small animal noises that was all around us. *¡Qué vida!* We talked about tonight when we would be at Lourdes Hall doing a slow rock with Rachel and Virgie. The date was to meet them at the hall in back of Our Lady of Lourdes Church. Everything was set. Tudi was going to borrow his *tío* Poncho's car. When we got back to Los, we would take a good bath and make it to the dance. Life is really good when you got a little wine, a good day for hunting doves, a chance to use a car, and a date with the two finest chicks in the barrio. *¡Hay, que si estaban buenas!*

My cousin Tudi lived across the street from my house. Besides Tudi, my *tía* Chelo had my cousins Neto and Fina, and a big white dog named Chico what bites tin cans and rocks for to keep his teeth sharp. And man, did that dog keep them sharp! Ask old Alfredo with his *nalgas razgadas.*

Later that afternoon, *cuando llegamos bien prendidos,* I went in my house knowing that Tudi would call me when it was time for the dance. I had only two doves, and I gave them to my mother. I didn't tell her that Tudi had shot both of them. So what if I was a lousy shot. Tonight I was going to show the *vatos* how to rock out, and Rachel how to make out. *¡Híjola!* My heart began to beat really fast. I made myself lighten up. Time for that later. Right now I was hungry, so I rolled myself some cold beans in a *tortilla* and sat outside on the old car seat under the fig tree, *contemplando las moscas* that gather because of the chickens.

Having finished my *refín,* I went to take my bath to get ready. And then was when my mother let all of the roof of the world fall on my head. She told me that Nicky Porras was coming for the chickens at seven o'clock. Me with a date in less than two hours and thirty-two chickens to clean and pluck! *Me lleva á la . . .* wait! *. . .* Tudi! Man, I went running out of the house yelling, "Tudi! . . . the chickens . . . Tudi!"

My *tía* Chelo came running out of the house, *muy apurada,* like when I fell and broke my arm. "*¿Qué pasa?*" she asked me.

"What happened?" *Me lleva á la . . .* "I got thirty-two chickens to kill, that's what happened!"

My *tía* then said, *con aquella paciencia,* "*¡Hay Chapito, cómo cres escandaloso!*"

"*¿Escandaloso?*" Me, with the chance of a lifetime vanishing in a bad dream of chickenshit, blood, and feathers; and she says *que soy escandaloso.* Trouble is some people don't really know what gots to be important in a growing *vato's* life.

Anyways, Tudi comes running out pulling up his counties. "Relax, *ese,*" he said, "we'll get it done in time. *¡Pinchis pollos!*"

When I think back to that time, it almost makes me sick because of what happened after that. First Tudi said to use my father's hatchet. It was very sharp for killing chickens. We tried to do it like an assembly line. I held the chicken and Tudi cut the neck. Only he missed. Man, he cut that chicken on the chest and it went running, squirting blood, and screaming like it was dying or something.

After that, we put a big *bote* to boil with water to soften the feathers for plucking. We put it on a fire made with sticks. Then we put the dead chickens in the water. Only some of the chickens wasn't dead. I complained, "Dammit Tudi, some of those chickens ain't dead, *ese!*"

"So what?" Tudi said, "they're going to die anyway, *ese!*" *Mi primo Tudi es muy gacho.*

Then there was smoke and fire and scared chickens; chickenshit on my shoes, blood on my hair, feathers in my mouth, and Tudi screaming at me, "Dammit Chapo! Hold that fucking chicken! I almost cut my hand, *loco!*"

Then we gave up with the dangerous hatchet. Next we were pulling their heads off by giving them the big twist in the air. The chickens would go flip-flopping all over the yard. Even the goat was covered with blood! I yelled at Tudi, *"Horale, loco,* you threw that chicken on the clothes line. You got my sister's *chones* full of blood, *ese!"*

But Tudi don't listen. His eyes were shiny and wide open. His face is sweating and he keeps on saying, "Hurry Chapo, hurry!" I ran to get another chicken. I tell you Rafas it was like the three stooges, but there was only two, me and Tudi. . . .

By the time we got to chicken number thirty-two, my arms hurt like the time we mixed cement for the basement. My head hurted and I'm for throwing up from the feathers and the blood. But we got them plucked. Each one, *loco.*

Now for a good hot bath and the dance. We are wiping off the feathers when Joey, what is Rachel and Virgie's little brother, comes in the yard. Joey is maybe a little bit *chiple* but he is good for bringing us messages from his sisters. I got a bad feeling about what he was going to tell us. He stopped and looked around at the feathers and the blood, then he smiled. Man, I don't like that smile. He started to giggle. *Oh shit!* "My father," said Joey, "says that because my cousin Sophie, what ain't married, is fat from a baby, my sisters can't go to no dances."

¡Que gacho! Sophie gets *pansona* and Virgie and Rachel can't go to the dance. That ain't right, *loco.* Everything happens to me. The chickens get plucked but no dance, no Rachel, no nothing. Tudi don't care. He went to the dance anyway. I don't feel like doing nothing. That Tudi, what a *vato.* Any babe is okay for him. Me? My mother is mad 'cause we only had twenty-nine chickens for Nicky. Two looked too ugly from the cuts on the chest, and one got left in the water too long and was almost cooked.

The warmth from my heart is gone. The warmth from my house and family is gone. Only the cold lights from the city below the barrio are left; the cold lights and the cold, dead chickens.

Well Rafas, that's the way it was. That night my mother fixed *Pollo en Mole* for dinner, but I wasn't too hungry . . . *tu sabes* . . . *Hay te watcho vato* . . . I don't feel too good,

Tu Camarada

El Chapo

Blue Bike Brings a Blue Day

Jerónimo G. Ortega

Chinto walked slowly, enjoying the afternoon as he headed
home. He had been out all morning selling the Sunday
Times. He had earned $4.50 and was happy because the
money would help keep food on the table until his Tio
Chuy received the check on the first of the month. He was
walking through the short cut he always took—over the
hills that formed a corona around the barrio. It was easier
to get home that way, easier than going around the hills
and then back up the valley. The grass was golden yellow
and the hillsides were trailed with slides the kids had grooved
out by sliding down the dry grass with cardboard. The area
at the bottom of the hill was cluttered with trash, cans and
old bed frames. Chinto usually stopped and lined up cans
on the bed frames and tested his arm by trying to knock
them down with rocks. But now he was eager to get home
to tell Tio Chuy about the money.

As he reached the bottom of the hill he walked over a
pile of cans to get to the dirt road that led to Tio Chuy's
house. Chinto would usually climb these piles and kick and
scatter as many of the cans as he could, then bust out running for home with all his might. But now he stopped. He
had noticed a two wheel bicycle frame sticking out among
all the junk. He bent down to examine the bicycle. The
front tire was twisted and the spokes stuck out at all angles.
It didn't have a seat, one of the pedals was missing, the
back tire was flat, and the bicycle chain was missing.

Chinto had never had a bike of his own, but he had
learned to ride one last summer when his primo, Fernando,
had taught him. His Tio Chuy couldn't afford to get him
one either. So now, as he looked at this wrecked bike, an
idea began to come to him. He would fix it. But he wondered how to explain the bike and the possibilites of repair-
ing it to Tio Chuy. Then he thought of it. He'd save 50¢ this
week and work harder next Sunday. In a few weeks he

would have enough money to fix the bike. And for now, he could paint it at least. Tío Chuy kept some leftover paint under the sink. It was light blue. He had used it in the bathroom and some was left. Chinto took the bike by the handlebars and, balancing it on the flat back tire, pushed and shoved it home, thinking happily of the babyblue-colored bike he would create as his own in a couple of weeks.

When he got to the house, he looked around for Tío Chuy. He saw him sitting near the side of the house, the shady side. He dragged the bike over.

"Tío Chuy," he said, "look what I found."

Tío Chuy looked up from the newspaper, *La Opinión,* and looked curiously at Chinto.

"¿Qué es, Chinto?" he asked.[1]

"A bicycle. I found it by the hill."

"¿Porqué la quieres? Está descompuesta," answered Tío Chuy.[2]

"Can I keep it?"

Tío Chuy shrugged his shoulders.

"I can fix it," Chinto pleaded. "I know it is broken, but if I sell more papers and save, in a few weeks I can have it ready."

Tío Chuy couldn't argue in the face of Chinto's excitement.

"Bueno, Chinto," he said, "Está bien. Vamos a ver si la podemos arreglar."[3]

Chinto wanted to get started right away.

"Tío, could we paint the bike right now? At least that? We can use the blue paint you have under the sink."

Tío Chuy nodded. "Sí. Ve tráimela."[4]

While Chinto went into the house, Tío Chuy dismantled the wheels and with a wire coat hanger, attached the frame to the large avocado tree in the yard. Chinto hurried back with the paint and they set to painting the bike with the light, skyblue paint. When they had finished, the bike was still only a frame, but Chinto was pleased with the result as he sat next to the frame and waited for the glistening paint to dry. Tío Chuy sat next to him, pleased at the boy's happi-

---

[1] "What is it, Chinto?"
[2] "Why do you want it? It's in pieces."
[3] "OK, Chinto. It's all right. Let's see if we can fix it."
[4] "Yes. Bring it to me."

ness and confident that Chinto would create a good bike for himself from this dangling frame.

The weeks passed, Chinto sold more papers each week, putting aside some money for the bike. Soon he had the tires, the chain and all the missing items except for the fenders. They cost more and he would have to be patient. But the bike could be ridden and he began to ride it all around the barrio, proud of it and enjoying showing it off to his friends. All he needed were the fenders to be completely proud of it.

As luck would have it, Chinto would be able to give all the money he was saving for the fenders to Tio Chuy for food. Chinto and some of the boys from the barrio were going one day to Morgan's trees. They were going there to get some loquats. They did this often, but this day as they were heading there, Chinto spotted some boxes and a large barrel of trash in an alley. He stopped when he noticed a light blue fender with a white eagle design painted on it jutting from the large barrel. He quickly pulled it out and inspected it. It was almost new. He looked into the barrel and found the front fender and a bicycle basket. The fenders matched! The basket would fit perfectly on his bike. He forgot about the loquats and carrying the fenders and basket, ran home to put them onto his own bike. He told Tio Chuy about his lucky find and gave him the money he had been saving. Tio Chuy was pleased and examined the fenders and basket. He smilingly told Chinto to hurry and put them on.

"Ahora que tiene canasta tu bicicleta," he said, "quiero que vayas a la tienda a un mandado. Nos sirve bien tu suerte." [5]

When he had finished assembling the bike, Chinto left the house and proudly pedaled his now whole bike through the barrio as he headed to the supermarket six blocks away. He was thinking how fortunate he was to have found those parts, almost new, how really lucky that they had been almost the same color and fit his bike perfectly. And the eagle design, it made him feel like a diving eagle as the wind swept by his face as he sped down the street. He was thinking about all of these things as he pulled up to a light a block away from the market. He was so deep in joy

[5] "Now that your bicycle has a basket, I want you to go to the store on an errand."

and thought that at first he didn't hear the woman's voice addressing him. But finally, when he noticed, he turned toward the curb and saw a tall, well dressed woman talking to him.

"Were you talking to me?" he asked.

The woman looked angry. "I asked you where you got that bike," she said, her voice harsh.

"It's mine," Chinto replied, watching the signal for the green light as he talked.

"Are you sure?" she asked.

"Sure, I'm sure. My Tio bought it for me." As soon as he said it, he felt he should have told the truth. But it was out now.

"Did he buy it for you with that eagle painted on the fender?" she asked, coming closer and looking at the design.

Chinto was beginning to feel uneasy. The way the women questioned and looked at him, he was starting to worry about having taken the fenders out of the barrel. Maybe they belonged to her or someone she knew. The woman finally straightened, just as Chinto noticed the light turn to green.

"This isn't your bike, little boy," she said. But he didn't hear, for he had pulled away from her and was speeding toward the market, leaving her yelling behind him.

In the market he hurried with Tio Chuy's mandado and trotted from the store to his bike. He had parked it behind the market, out of sight. But as he was running toward it, he saw the woman. She was standing by the bike, her hand on top of the seat.

"You stole this bike," she said, as he came up.

"No, I didn't. It's mine."

He put his package in the basket and tried to wrestle the bike away from her. "It's mine, it's mine," he kept yelling.

"You give me this bike, you thieving Mexican," the lady screamed. "It belongs to my son. That's his eagle painted on the fender."

Chinto tried the truth.

"Lady, I didn't steal your son's bike," he pleaded. "I found it and fixed it, so it belongs to me. It's mine. I found it at the dump." He felt tears forming. The lady wasn't believing him and held onto the bike.

"You're a liar!" she screamed. "Nobody would throw a bike like this away."

A group of people had gathered around. The lady yelled at them to call the cops. Chinto, really afraid and confused now, began to drag the bike away from the woman. She wouldn't let go. Suddenly a strong arm grabbed Chinto from behind and held him tight.

"He's a thief, he stole my son's bike," the woman yelled. The man had Chinto by the back of the neck.

"You'd better stay still, punk," the man was saying as he squeezed, "or I'm gonna break your Mexican neck." Chinto was terrified and stayed still. He tried to plead with the tall white man.

"She don't know what she's talking about, mister. It's my bike. I found it and fixed it. You can ask my Tio Chuy . . . he knows."

"Shaddup you thieving little . . . " the man didn't finish for a patrol car had pulled up. A big redfaced policeman got out on one side, a younger one on the other. The young one came over and took a hold of Chinto, thanking the tall white man for holding him, while the redfaced one spoke to the woman. Chinto could hear her telling him about the bike.

"It's a lie," he yelled. "It's my bike!" The policeman holding him slapped him across the face.

"Don't you talk to people like that. Learn how to respect," he said, tightening his grip on Chinto's arm.

The blow hurt and Chinto covered his face with his hands and swore softly into his hands. He was furious and bewildered. He felt like breaking the bike, every last spoke and piece of metal of it over the heads of the cops and the woman and the tall man. But all he could finally do was cry.

The older policeman came over. The lady stood behind him and glared at Chinto.

"Let's take him in," he said to the policeman holding Chinto.

Chinto tried desperately to convince them they were wrong. "I found it," he cried. "I didn't steal it. Ask my Uncle Chuy. He'll tell you."

The older policeman spoke to him. "This guy, your uncle, you live with him?"

Chinto nodded. "He knows the true story. He helped me fix the bike."

The big cop turned toward the woman. "We're going to check it out. It's routine. We'll get you your bike."

They put the bike into the trunk of the patrol car and hustled Chinto in. He told them where he lived and they left the market parking lot. Through the open window Chinto had heard the woman damning all these "Mexican" punks for not letting decent people live in peace.

At Tio Chuy's house, the police pushed Chinto from the car and up the steps and knocked on the door. Tio Chuy opened the door, surprised as he saw who it was.

"Are you this kid's uncle?" the redfaced policeman asked Tio Chuy.

Tio Chuy nodded.

"He claims he found a bike. We think he stole it. What do you know about it?"

Tio Chuy picked his words carefully. "I no speak no good ingles, but my Chinto no stole no bike. He good boy, very good. He work, sell papers, fix bicicleta. No, no señor, Chinto no stole."

The younger one spoke up.

"Look, mister. A lady says it's her son's bike. She's identified it. That means that this kid is telling a lie."

Tio Chuy started to protest, but the policeman wasn't listening.

"I think you people ought to watch your kids better," he continued, "so they don't go around stealing everything that isn't nailed down. You're supposed to be responsible for them."

Tio Chuy could only utter that Chinto was a good boy, that he wouldn't steal.

"We're taking him with us," the older policeman said. "You can pick him up at Juvenile Hall where he belongs."

Tio Chuy stopped them. "No, señores. El es muy chico . . . too small for jail . . . Leave him, por favor. He good boy, he no stole bike."

The younger one shook his head. "We're going to teach him not to steal."

Tio Chuy tried one last desparate plea, he would speak the lie that they waited for.

"Wait. O.K., o.k. Maybe my sobrino stole the bike. I fix him . . . he will not steal again, o.k.? Por favor, no jail. I take care of him."

The policemen looked at each other.

The older one nodded. "Just make sure that you do take care of him. We have a place for kids like this so don't let him go around stealing. Comprende?"

Tio Chuy feigned gratitude. "Gracias, señor. Gracias." But there was hatred in his eyes.

Chinto had been too confused and shaken to follow the conversation between his uncle and the policemen closely. He had thought that Tio Chuy had it all settled.

"Can I get my bike now, Mr. Policeman?" he asked.

"No. You stole that bike and we're taking it to the rightful owner. I'm giving you a chance this time, but you better not steal again." As the older policeman was saying this he had Chinto by the shoulder, and he squeezed hard, hurting. "Understand?" he said.

Chinto was silent. Then began to protest. "But—" he began. But Tio Chuy stopped him.

"Déjalo, Chinto. No se puede hacer nada." [6]

"Remember what we said," the younger one yelled back to Tio Chuy as they headed down the steps. "Keep him out of trouble."

They got into their car and pulled away, their tires screeching as they shot out of the yard. Chinto was too stunned to speak as he watched his bike disappear with the patrol car. Then he looked up at Tio Chuy, tears streaming down his face.

"Tio Chuy. Why didn't they believe me? Why did you let them take my bike? Why didn't you tell them?"

Tio Chuy put his hand on Chinto's head. "Hijo, yo sé que no te la robaste, pero no pude dejarque te llevaran a la carcel. Con ellos no se puede discutir." [7]

Chinto's tears rolled freely as he watched the disappearing patrol car. He couldn't understand any of it. All he knew was that it was his bike and they'd taken it away from him. Next to him, Tio Chuy stared after the car with anger and hatred and frustration welling up in him. He was feeling very sorry for Chinto. For he knew that even if he could say something to Chinto, there would never be enough money in his monthly check to get Chinto another bike.

---

[6] "Leave it, Chinto. You can't do anything."
[7] "Son, I know you didn't steal it, but I couldn't let them take you to jail. You can't talk to them."

from *Barrio Boy*

Ernesto Galarza

To make room for a growing family it was decided that we should move, and a house was found in Oak Park, on the far side of town where the open country began. The men raised the first installment for the bungalow on Seventh Avenue even after Mrs. Dodson explained that if we did not keep up the monthly payments we would lose the deposit as well as the house.

The real estate broker brought the sale contract to the apartment one evening. Myself included, we sat around the table in the living room, the gringo explaining at great length the small print of the document in a torrent of words none of us could make out. Now and then he would pause and throw in the only word he knew in Spanish: "Sabee?" The men nodded slightly as if they had understood. Doña Henriqueta was holding firmly to the purse which contained the down payment, watching the broker's face, not listening to his words. She had only one question. Turning to me she said: "Ask him how long it will take to pay all of it." I translated, shocked by the answer: "Twenty years." There was a long pause around the table, broken by my stepfather: "What do you say?" Around the table the heads nodded agreement. The broker passed his fountain pen to him. He signed the contract and after him Gustavo and José. Doña Henriqueta opened the purse and counted out the greenbacks. The broker pocketed the money, gave us a copy of the document, and left.

The last thing I did when we moved out of 418 L was to dig a hole in the corner of the backyard for a tall carton of Quaker Oats cereal, full to the brim with the marbles I had won playing for keeps around the *barrio*. I tamped the earth over my buried treasure and laid a curse on whoever removed it without my permission.

Our new bungalow had five rooms, and porches front and back. In the way of furniture, what friends did not lend or Mrs. Dodson gave us we bought in the second-hand shops. The only new item was an elegant gas range, with a high oven and long, slender legs finished in enamel. Like the house, we would be paying for it in installments.

It was a sunny, airy spot, with a family orchard to one side and a vacant lot on the other. Back of us there was a pasture. With chicken wire we fenced the back yard, turned over the soil, and planted our first vegetable garden and fruit trees. José and I built a palatial rabbit hutch of laths and two-by-fours he gathered day by day on the waterfront. A single row of geraniums and carnations separated the vegetable garden from the house. From the vacant lots and pastures around us my mother gathered herbs and weeds which she dried and boiled the way she had in the pueblo. A thick green fluid she distilled from the mallow that grew wild around us was bottled and used as a hair lotion. On every side our windows looked out on family orchards, platinum stretches of wild oats and quiet lanes, shady and unpaved.

We could not have moved to a neighborhood less like the *barrio*. All the families around us were Americans. The grumpy retired farmer next door viewed us with alarm and never gave us the time of day, but the Harrisons across the street were cordial. Mr. Harrison loaned us his tools, and Roy, just my age but twice my weight, teamed up with me at once for an exchange of visits to his mother's kitchen and ours. I astounded him with my Mexican rice, and Mrs. Harrison baked my first waffle. Roy and I also found a common bond in the matter of sisters. He had an older one and by now I had two younger ones. It was a question between us whether they were worse as little nuisances or as big bosses. The answer didn't make much difference but it was a relief to have another man to talk with.

Some Sundays we walked to Joyland, an amusement park where my mother sat on a bench to watch the children play on the lawn and I begged as many rides as I could on the roller coaster, which we called in elegant Spanish "the Russian Mountain." José liked best the free vaudeville because of the chorus girls who danced out from the stage on a platform and kicked their heels over his head.

Since Roy had a bicycle and could get away from his sister by pedaling off on long journeys I persuaded my family to match my savings for a used one. Together we pushed beyond the boundaries of Oak Park miles out, nearly to Perkins and the Slough House. It was open country, where we could lean our wheels against a fence post and walk endlessly through carpets of golden poppies and blue lupin. With a bike I was able to sign on as a carrier of the *Sacramento Bee,* learning in due course the art of slapping folded newspapers against people's porches instead of into the bushes or on their roofs. Roy and I also became assistants to a neighbor who operated a bakery in his basement, taking our pay partly in dimes and partly in broken cookies for our families.

For the three men of the household as well as for me the bicycle became the most important means for earning a living. Oak Park was miles away from the usual places where they worked and they pedaled off, in good weather and bad, in the early morning. It was a case of saving carfare.

I transferred to the Bret Harte School, a gingerbread two-story building in which there was a notable absence of Japanese, Filipinos, Koreans, Italians, and the other nationalities of the Lincoln School. It was at Bret Harte that I learned how an English sentence could be cut up on the blackboard and the pieces placed on different lines connected by what the teacher called a diagram. The idea of operating on a sentence and rearranging its members as a skelton of verbs, modifiers, subject, and prepositions set me off diagraming whatever I read, in Spanish and English. Spiderwebs, my mother called them, when I tried to teach her the art.

My bilingual library had grown with some copies of old magazines from Mexico, a used speller Gustavo had bought for me in Stockton, and the novels my mother discarded when she had read them. Blackstone was still the anchor of my collection and I now had a paperback dictionary called *El Inglés sin Maestro.* By this time there was no problem of translating or interpreting for the family I could not tackle with confidence.

It was Gustavo, in fact, who began to give my books a vague signifiance. He pointed out to me that with diagrams and dictionaries I could have a choice of becoming a lawyer or a doctor or an engineer or a professor. These, he said, were far better careers than growing up to be a *camello,* as he and José always would be. *Camellos,* I knew well enough, was what the *chicanos* called themselves as the

worker on every job who did the dirtiest work. And to
give our home the professional touch he felt I should be
acquiring, he had a telephone installed.

It came to the rest of us as a surprise. The company man
arrived one day with our name and address on a card, a
metal tool box and a stand-up telephone wound with a cord.
It was connected and set on the counter between the dining
room and the parlor. There the black marvel sat until we
were gathered for dinner that evening. It was clearly explained by Gustavo that the instrument was to provide me
with a quick means of reaching the important people I
knew at the Y.M.C.A., the boy's band, or the various
public offices where I interpreted for *chicanos* in distress.
Sooner or later some of our friends in the *barrio* would
also have telephones and we could talk with them.

"Call somebody," my mother urged me.

With the whole family watching I tried to think of some
important person I could ring for a professional conversation. A name wouldn't come. I felt miserable and hardly
like a budding engineer or lawyer or doctor or professor.

Gustavo understood my predicament and let me stew in
it a moment. Then he said: "Mrs. Dodson." My pride
saved by this ingenious suggestion, I thumbed through the
directory, lifted the earpiece from the hook, and calmly
asked central for the number. My sisters, one sitting on the
floor and the other in my mother's arms, never looked less
significant; but they, too, had their turn saying hello to the
patient Señora Dodson on the other end of the line.

Every member of the family, in his own way, missed the
barrio. José and Gustavo could no longer join the talk of
the poolrooms and the street corners by walking two blocks
down the street. The sign language and simple words my
mother had devised to communicate with the Americans
at 418 L didn't work with the housewives on 7th Avenue.
The families we had known were now too far away to exchange visits. We knew no one in Oak Park who spoke
Spanish. Our street was always quiet and often lonely with
little to watch from our front porch other than boys riding
bicycles or Mrs. Harrison hanging out her wash. Pork
Chops and the Salvation Army never played there.

I, too, knew that things were different. There was no
corner where I could sell the *Union* and my income from
running errands and doing chores around the rooming
house stopped. There were no alleys I could comb for beer

bottles or docks where I could gather saleable or edible things. The closest to Big Singh I could find was a runty soothsayer in Joyland who sat on a rug with a feather in his turban and told your fortune.

We now had an infant boy in the family who with my two sisters made four of us. The baby was himself no inconvenience to me, but it meant that I had to mind the girls more, mostly chasing them home from the neighbors. If I had been the eldest girl in the family I would have stepped into my mother's place and taken over the management of all but the youngest. But being a boy, the female chores seemed outrageous and un-Mexican. Doña Henriqueta tried telling me that I was now the *jefe de familia* of all the juniors. But she was a gentle mother and the freedom of the house, the yard, and my personal property that she gave the two girls did nothing to make them understand that I was their *jefe*. When Nora, the oldest of the two, demolished my concertina with a hammer (no doubt to see where the notes came from) I asked for permission to strangle her. Permission was denied.

During the first year we lived at Oak Park we began to floor and partition the basement. Some day, we knew, the Lopez's would come through and we would have a temporary home ready for them. With three-and-a-half men in the house earning wages, if work was steady, we were keeping up with the installments and saving for the reunion.

An epidemic erased the quiet life on 7th Avenue and the hopes we had brought with us.

I had been reading to the family stories in the *Bee* of the Spanish influenza. At first it was far off, like the war, in places such as New York and Texas. Then the stories told of people dying in California towns we knew, and finally the *Bee* began reporting the spread of the "flu" in our city.

One Sunday morning we saw Gustavo coming down the street with a suitcase in his hand, walking slowly. I ran out to meet him. By the front gate, he dropped the suitcase, leaned on the fence, and fainted. He had been working as a sandhog on the American River, and had come home weak from fever.

Gustavo was put to bed in one of the front rooms. José set out to look for a doctor, who came the next day, weary and nearly sick himself. He ordered Gustavo to the hospital. Three days later I answered the telephone call from the hospital telling us he was dead. Only José went to Gustavo's funeral. The rest of us, except my stepfather, were sick in bed with the fever.

In the dining room, near the windows where the sunlight would warm her, my mother lay on a cot, a kerosene stove at her feet. The day Gustavo died she was delirious. José bicycled all over the city, looking for oranges, which the doctor said were the best medicine we could give her. I sweated out the fever, nursed by José, who brought me glasses of steaming lemonade and told me my mother was getting better. The children were quarantined in another room, lightly touched by the fever, more restless than sick.

Late one afternoon José came into my room, wrapped me in blankets, pulled a cap over my ears, and carried me to my mother's bedside. My stepfather was holding a hand mirror to her lips. It didn't fog. She had stopped breathing. In the next room my sister was singing to the other children, "A birdie with a yellow bill/ hopped upon my windowsill/ cocked a shiny eye and said/ Shame on you you sleepy head."

The day we buried Doña Henriqueta, Mrs. Dodson took the oldest sister home with her. The younger children were sent to a neighbor. That night José went to the *barrio*, got drunk, borrowed a pistol, and was arrested for shooting up Second Street.

We did not find out what had happened until I bicycled the next morning to Mrs. Dodson to report that José had not come home. By this time our friends in the *barrio* knew of José's arrest and a telephone call to a bartender who knew us supplied the details. Nothing serious, Mrs. Dodson repeated to me. Nobody had been hurt. She left me in charge of my sister and went to bail out my uncle.

They returned together. Gently, Mrs. Dodson scolded José, who sat dejectedly, his eyes closed so he would not have to look her in the eye, cracking the joint of his fingers, chewing on his tight lips, a young man compressing years of hard times and the grief of the past days in a show of manhood.

When the lecture was nearly over, Mrs. Dodson was not talking of drunkenness and gunplay, but of the future, mostly of mine, and of José's responsibility for it. She walked with us down the front stairway. Pushing my bicycle I followed him on foot the miles back to Oak Park, keeping my distance, for I knew he did not want me to see his face. As he had often told me, "Men never cry, no matter what."

A month later I made a bundle of the family keepsakes my stepfather allowed me to have, including the butterfly sarape, my books, and some family pictures. With the bundle tied to the bars of my bicycle, I pedaled to the basement room José had rented for the two of us on O Street near the corner of Fifth, on the edge of the *barrio*.

José was now working the riverboats and, in the slack season, following the round of odd jobs about the city. In our basement room, with a kitchen closet, bathroom, and laundry tub on the back porch and a woodshed for storage, I kept house. We bought two cots, one for me and the other for José when he was home.

Our landlords lived upstairs, a middle-aged brother and sister who worked and rented rooms. As part payment on our rent I kept the yard trim. They were friends of Doña Tránsito, the grandmother of a Mexican family that lived in a weather-beaten cottage on the corner. Doña Tránsito was in her sixties, round as a barrel, and she wore her gray hair in braids and smoked hand-rolled cigarettes on her rickety front porch. To her tiny parlor *chicanos* in trouble came for advice, and the firm old lady with the rasping voice and commanding ways often asked me to interpret or translate for them in their encounters with the *Autoridades*. Since her services were free, so were mine. I soon became a regular visitor and made friends with her son, Kid Felix, a prizefighter who gave free boxing lessons to the boys in the neighborhood.

Living only three houses from Doña Tránsito, saying my *saludos* to her every time I passed the corner, noticing how even the Kid was afraid to break her personal code of *barrio* manners, I lived inside a circle of security when José was away. On her front porch, summer evenings, the old Mexican dame talked about people such as I had known in the pueblo and asked how I was doing in school and where I was working.

It was Doña Tránsito who called in the *curandera* once when the child of a neighbor was dying. I had brought a doctor to the house and was in the sick room when he told the family there was nothing more he could do. Doña Tránsito ordered me at once to fetch the old crone who lived on the other side of the railroad tracks towards the river and who practiced as a healer.

With Doña Tránsito I watched the ritual from a corner
of the sick room. The healer laid on a side table an assortment of bundled weeds, small glass jars, candles, and paper
bags tied with strings. On the floor next to her she placed
a canvas satchel. A bowl and some cups were brought to
her from the kitchen. She crumpled stems of herbs into
one of the cups and mixed them with oil from one of her
jars. She hooked her finger into another jar and pulled out
a dab of lard which she worked into a powder in another
cup to make a dark paste. Two candles were lighted and
placed at the head of the bed. The electric light was turned
off. She opened the satchel and took out a framed picture of
the Virgin of Guadalupe, which was hung on the wall over
the sick child's head. The window blind pulled down.

The little girl was uncovered. She lay naked, pale and
thin on the sheet, her arms straight down her sides. Around
her the healer arranged a border of cactus leaves, which
she took out of her satchel one by one, cutting them open
around the edge. She warmed the cup with the powdered
herbs and rubbed the concoction on the soles of the child's
bare feet. With the paste, which she also warmed over the
candle, the healer made a cross on the forehead of the
patient and another on her chest. A blanket was then laid
over her, leaving only the head uncovered.

The healer knelt before the picture of the Virgin and
began to pray. The parents of the child, some relatives who
were there, Doña Tránsito and I formed a circle around the
room, on our knees.

We had been praying a long while when the healer arose
and bent over the bed, looking intently at the wasted face.
To nobody in particular she said the child was not sweating.
She wrapped her black shawl around her head and
shoulders, left the room, and closed the street door quietly
behind her. In the morning the child died.

Through Doña Tránsito I met other characters of the
barrio. One of them was Don Crescencio, stooped and bony,
who often stopped to chat with my neighbor. He told
us stories of how he had found buried treasure with two
twigs cut from a weeping willow, and how he could locate
an underground spring in the same way, holding the twigs
just so, feeling his way on bare feet over the ground, watching until the twigs, by themselves, crossed and dipped.
There were the Ortegas, who raised vegetables on a sandlot
they had bought by the levee, and explained to Doña Trán-

sito, who knew a great deal about such matters herself, what vegetables did better when planted according to different shapes of the moon. The Kid gave us lectures and exhibitions explaining jabs and left hooks and how he planned to become the world's Mexican champion. In our basement José gathered his friends to listen to songs of love, revenge, and valor, warmed with beer and tequila.

When troubles made it necessary for the *barrio* people to deal with the Americans uptown, the *Autoridades,* I went with them to the police court, the industrial accident office, the county hospital, the draft board, the county clerk. We got lost together in the rigamarole of functionaries who sat, like *patrones,* behind desks and who demanded licenses, certificates, documents, affidavits, signatures, and witnesses. And we celebrated our successes, as when the worker for whom I interpreted in interviews that lasted many months, was awarded a thousand dollars for a disabled arm. Don Crescencio congratulated me, saying that in Mexico for a thousand American dollars you could buy the lives of many peons.

José had chosen our new home in the basement on O Street because it was close to the Hearkness Junior High School, to which I transferred from Bret Harte. As the *jefe de familia* he explained that I could help earn our living but that I was to study for a high school diploma. That being settled, my routine was clearly divided into schooltime and worktime, the second depending on when I was free from the first.

Few Mexicans of my age from the *barrio* were enrolled at the junior high school when I went there. At least, there were no other Mexican boys or girls in Mr. Everett's class in civics, or Miss Crowley's English composition, or Mrs. Stevenson's course. Mrs. Stevenson assigned me to read to the class and to recite poems by Amado Nervo, because the poet was from Tepic and I was, too. Miss Crowley accepted my compositions about Jalcocotán and the buried treasure of Acaponeta while the others in the class were writing about Sir Patrick Spence and the Beautiful Lady without Mercy, whom they had never met. For Mr. Everett's class, the last of the day, I clipped pieces from the *Sacramento Bee* about important events in Sacramento. From him I learned to use the ring binder in which I kept clippings to prepare oral reports. Occasionally he kept me after school to talk. He sat on his desk, one leg dangling over a corner,

behind him the frame of a large window and the arching
elms of the school yard, telling me he thought I could easily
make the debating team at the high school next year, that
Stanford University might be the place to go after graduation, and making other by-the-way comments that began to
shape themselves into my future.

Afternoons, Saturdays, and summers allowed me many
hours of worktime I did not need for study. José explained
how things now stood. There were two funerals to pay for.
More urgently than ever, Doña Esther and her family must
be brought to live with us. He would pay the rent and buy
the food. My clothes, books and school expenses would
be up to me.

On my vacations, and when he was not on the riverboats,
he found me a job as water boy on a track gang. We chopped
wood together near Woodland and stacked empty lug
boxes in a cannery yard. Cleaning vacant houses and chopping weeds were jobs we could do as a team when better
ones were not to be had. As the apprentice, I learned from
him how to brace myself for a heavy lift, to lock my knee
under a loaded handtruck, to dance rather than lift a ladder
and to find the weakest grain in a log. Like him I spit into
my palms to get the feel of the axe handle and grunted as
the blade bit into the wood. Imitating him I circled a tree
several times, sizing it up, *tanteando,* as he said, before
pruning or felling it.

Part of one summer my uncle worked on the river while
I hired out a farmhand on a small ranch south of Sacramento. My senior on the place was Roy, a husky Oklaho-
man who was part-time taxi driver and full-time drinker
of hard whiskey. He was heavy-chested, heavy-lipped and
jowly, a grumbler rather than a talker and a man of great
ingenuity with tools and automobile engines. Under him I
learned to drive the Fordson tractor on the place, man the
gasoline pump, feed the calves, check an irrigation ditch,
make lug boxes for grapes and many other tasks on a
small farm. Roy used Bull Durham tobacco which he rolled
into the same droopy cigarettes that Doña Eduvijes smoked
in Jalco and Doña Tránsito on her front porch.

Roy and I sat under the willow tree in front of the ranch
house after work, I on the grass, he on a creaky wicker
chair, a hulking, sour man glad for the company of a boy.
He counseled me on how to avoid the indulgences he was
so found of, beginning his sentences with a phrase he re-

peated over and over, "as the feller says." "Don't aim to tell you your business," he explained, "but, as the feller says, get yourself a good woman, don't be no farmhand for a livin', be a lawyer or a doctor, and don't get to drinkin' nohow. And there's another thing, Ernie. If nobody won't listen to you, go on and talk to yourself and hear what a smart man has to say."

And Roy knew how to handle boys, which he showed in an episode that could have cost me my life or my self-confidence. He had taught me to drive the tractor, walking along side during the lessons as I maneuvered it, shifting gears, stopping and starting, turning and backing, raising a cloud of dust wherever we went. Between drives Roy told me about the different working parts of the machine, giving me instructions on oiling and greasing and filling the radiator. "She needs to be took care of, Ernie," he admonished me, "like a horse. And another thing, she's like to buck. She can turn clear over on you if you let 'er. If she starts to lift from the front even a mite, you turn her off. You hear?"

"Yes, sir," I said, meaning to keep his confidence in me as a good tractor man.

It was a few days after my first solo drive that it happened. I was rounding a telephone pole on the slightly sloping bank of the irrigation ditch. I swung around too fast for one of rear tracks to keep its footing. It spun and the front began to lift. Forgetting Roy's emphatic instructions I gunned the engine, trying to right us to the level ground above the ditch. The tractor's nose kept climbing in front of me. We slipped against the pole, the tractor, bucking, as Roy said it would.

Roy's warning broke through to me in my panic, and I reached up to turn off the ignition. My bronco's engine sputtered out and it settled on the ground with a thump.

I sat for a moment in my sweat. Roy was coming down the ditch in a hurry. He walked up to me and with a quick look saw that neither I nor the tractor was damaged.

"Git off" he said.

I did, feeling that I was about to be demoted, stripped of my rank, bawled out, and fired.

Roy mounted the machine, started it, and worked it off the slope to flat ground. Leaving the engine running, he said: "Git on."

I did.

"Now finish the discing," he said. Above the clatter of the machine, he said: "Like I said, she can buck. If she does, cut 'er. You hear?" And he waved me off to my work.

Except for food and a place to live, with which José provided me, I was on my own. Between farm jobs I worked in town, adding to my experience as well as to my income. As a clerk in a drug store on Second and J, in the heart of the lower part of town, I waited on *chicanos* who spoke no English and who came in search of remedies with no prescription other than a recital of their pains. I dispensed capsules, pills, liniments, and emulsions as instructed by the pharmacist, who glanced at our customers from the back of the shop and diagnosed their ills as I translated them. When I went on my shift, I placed a card in the window that said 'Se habla Español." So far as my *chicano* patients were concerned it might as well have said "Dr. Ernesto Galarza."

From drugs I moved to office supplies and stationery sundries, working as delivery boy for Wahl's, several blocks uptown from skid row. Between deliveries I had no time to idle. I helped the stock clerk, took inventory, polished desks, and hopped when a clerk bawled an order down the basement steps. Mr. Wahl, our boss, a stocky man with a slight paunch, strutted a little as he constantly checked on the smallest details of his establishment, including myself. He was always pleasant and courteous, a man in whose footsteps I might possibly walk into the business world of Sacramento.

But like my uncles, I was looking for a better *chanza*, which I thought I found with Western Union, as a messenger, where I could earn tips as well as wages. Since I knew the lower part of town thoroughly, whenever the telegrams were addressed to that quarter the dispatcher gave them to me. Deliveries to the suites on the second floor of saloons paid especially well, with tips of a quarter from the ladies who worked there. My most generous customer was tall and beautiful Miss Irene, who always asked how I was doing in school. It was she who gave me an English dictionary, the first I ever possessed, a black bound volume with remarkable little scallops on the pages that made it easy to find words. Half smiling, half commanding, Miss Irene said to me more than once: "Don't you stop school without letting me know." I meant to take her advice as earnestly as I took her twenty-five cent tip.

It was in the lower town also that I nearly became a

performing artist. My instructor on the violin had stopped
giving me lessons after we moved to Oak Park. When we
were back on O Street he sent word through José that I
could work as second fiddler on Saturday nights in the
dancehall where he played with a mariachi. Besides, I could
resume my lessons with him. A dollar a night for two hours
as a substitute was the best wages I had ever made. Coached
by my teacher, I second-fiddled for sporting *chicanos* who
swung their ladies on the dance floor and sang to our music.
Unfortunately I mentioned my new calling to Miss Crowley
when I proposed it to her as a subject for a composition.
She kept me after school and persuaded me to give it up, on
the ground that I could earn more decorating Christmas
cards during the vacation than at the dancehall. She gave
me the first order for fifty cards and got subscriptions for
me from the other teachers. I spent my Christmas vacation
as an illustrator, with enough money saved to quit playing
in the saloon.

It was during the summer vacation that school did not
interfere with making a living, the time of the year when I
went with other *barrio* people to the ranches to look for
work. Still too young to shape up with the day-haul gangs,
I loitered on skid row, picking up conversation and reading
the chalk signs about work that was being offered. For a
few days of picking fruit or pulling hops I bicycled to Folsom, Lodi, Woodland, Freeport, Walnut Grove, Marysville,
Slough House, Florin, and places that had no name. Looking for work, I pedaled through a countryside blocked off,
mile after mile, into orchards, vineyards, and vegetable
farms. Along the ditchbanks, where the grass, the morning
glory, and the wild oats made a soft mattress I unrolled my
bindle and slept.

In the labor camps I shared the summertime of the lives
of the *barrio* people. They gathered from barrios of faraway places like Imperial Valley, Los Angeles, Phoenix,
and San Antonio. Each family traveling on its own, they
came in trucks piled with household goods or packed in
their secondhand *fotingos* and *chevees*. The trucks and cars
were ancient models, fresh out of a used-car lot, with
license tags of many states. It was into these jalopies that
much of the care and a good part of the family's earnings
went. In camp they were constantly being fixed, so close to
scrap that when we needed a part for repairs, we first went
to the nearest junkyard.

It was a world different in so many ways from the lower

part of Sacramento and the residences surrounded by trim lawns and cool canopies of elms to which I had delivered packages for Wahl's. Our main street was usually an irrigation ditch, the water supply for cooking, drinking, laundering, and bathing. In the better camps there was a faucet or a hydrant, from which water was carried in buckets, pails and washtubs. If the camp belonged to a contractor, and it was used from year to year, there were permanent buildings —a shack for his office, the privies, weatherworn and sagging, and a few cabins made of secondhand lumber, patched and unpainted.

If the farmer provided housing himself, it was in tents pitched on the bare baked earth or on the rough ground of newly plowed land on the edge of a field. Those who arrived late for the work season camped under trees or raised lean-to's along a creek, roofing their trucks with canvas to make bedrooms. Such camps were always well away from the house of the ranchero, screened from the main road by an orchard or a grove of eucalyptus. I helped to pitch and take down such camps, on some spot that seemed lonely when we arrived, desolate when we left.

If they could help it, the workers with families avoided the more permanent camps, where the seasonal hired hands from skid row were more likely to be found. I lived a few days in such a camp and found out why families avoided them. On Saturday nights when the crews had a week's wages in their pockets, strangers appeared, men and women, carrying suitcases with liquor and other contraband. The police were called by the contractor only when the carousing threatened to break into fighting. Otherwise, the weekly bouts were a part of the regular business of the camp.

Like all the others, I often went to work without knowing how much I was going to be paid. I was never hired by a rancher, but by a contractor or a straw boss who picked up crews in town and handled the payroll. The important questions that were in my mind—the wages per hour or per lug box, whether the beds would have mattresses and blankets, the price of meals, how often we would be paid— were never discussed, much less answered, beforehand. Once we were in camp, owing the employer for the ride to the job, having no means to get back to town except by walking and no money for the next meal, arguments over working conditions were settled in favor of the boss. I learned firsthand the chiseling techniques of the contractors and their pushers—how they knocked off two or three lugs of grapes from the daily record for each member of the crew, or the way they had of turning the face of the scales away from you when you weighed your work in.

There was never any doubt about the contractor and his power over us. He could fire a man and his family on the spot and make them wait days for their wages. A man could be forced to quit by assigning him regularly to the thinnest pickings in the field. The worst thing one could do was to ask for fresh water on the job, regardless of the heat of the day; instead of iced water, given freely, the crews were expected to buy sodas at twice the price in town, sold by the contractor himself. He usually had a pistol—to protect the payroll, so it was said. Through the ranchers for whom he worked, we were certain that he had connections with the *Autoridades,* for they never showed up in camp to settle wage disputes or listen to our complaints or to go for a doctor when one was needed. Lord of a rag-tag labor camp of Mexicans, the contractor, a Mexican himself, knew that few men would let their anger blow, even when he stung them with curses like, "Orale, San Afabeeches huevones."

As a single worker, I usually ate with some household, paying for my board. I did more work than a child but less than a man, neither the head nor the tail of a family. Unless the camp was a large one I became acquainted with most of the families. Those who could not write asked me to chalk their payroll numbers on the boxes they picked. I counted matches for a man who transferred them from the right pocket of his pants to the left as he tallied the lugs he filled throughout the day. It was his only check on the record the contractor kept of his work. As we worked the rows or the tree blocks during the day, or talked in the evenings where the men gathered in small groups to smoke and rest, I heard about *barrios* I had never seen but that must have been much like ours in Sacramento.

The only way to complain or protest was to leave, but now and then a camp would stand instead of run, and for a few hours or a few days work would slow down or stop. I saw it happen in a pear orchard in Yolo when pay rates were cut without notice to the crew. The contractor said the market for pears had dropped and the rancher could not afford to pay more. The fruit stayed on the trees, while we, a committee drafted by the camp, argued with the contractor first and then with the rancher. The talks gave them time to round up other pickers. A carload of police in plain clothes drove into the camp. We were lined up for our pay, taking whatever the contractor said was on his books. That afternoon we were ordered off the ranch.

In a camp near Folsom, during hop picking, it was not wages but death that pulled the people together. Several children in the camp were sick with diarrhea; one had been taken to the hospital in town and the word came back that he had died. It was the women who guessed that the cause of the epidemic was the water. For cooking and drinking and washing it came from a ditch that went by the ranch stables upstream.

I was appointed by a camp committee to go to Sacramento to find some *Autoridad* who would send an inspector. Pedaling my bicycle, mulling over where to go and what to say, I remembered some clippings from the *Sacramento Bee* that Mr. Everett had discussed in class, and I decided the man to look for was Mr. Simon Lubin, who was in some way a state *Autoridad*.

He received me in his office at Weinstock and Lubin's. He sat, square-shouldered and natty, behind a desk with a glass top. He was half-bald, with a strong nose and a dimple in the center of his chin. To his right was a box with small levers into which Mr. Lubin talked and out of which came voices.

He heard me out, asked me questions and made notes on a pad. He promised that an inspector would come to the camp. I thanked him and thought the business of my visit was over; but Mr. Lubin did not break the handshake until he had said to tell the people in the camp to organize. Only by organizing, he told me, will they ever have decent places to live.

I reported the interview with Mr. Lubin to the camp. The part about the inspector they understood and it was voted not to go back to work until he came. The part about organizing was received in silence and I knew they understood it as little as I did. Remembering Duran in that camp meeting, I made my first organizing speech.

The inspector came and a water tank pulled by mules was parked by the irrigation ditch. At the same time the contractor began to fire some of the pickers. I was one of them. I finished that summer nailing boxes on a grape ranch near Florin.

When my job ended I pedaled back to Sacramento, detouring over country lanes I knew well. Here and there I walked the bicycle over dirt roads rutted by wagons. The pastures were sunburned and the grain fields had been cut to stubble. Riding by a thicket of reeds where an irrigation ditch swamped I stopped and looked at the red-winged blackbirds riding gracefully on the tips of the canes. Now and then they streaked out of the green clump, spraying the pale sky with crimson dots in all directions.

Crossing the Y Street levee by Southside Park I rode through the *barrio* to Doña Tránsito's, leaving my bike hooked on the picket fence by the handle bar.

I knocked on the screen door that always hung tired, like the sagging porch coming unnailed. No one was at home.

It was two hours before time to cook supper. From the stoop I looked up and down the cross streets. The *barrio* seemed empty.

I unhooked the bicycle, mounted it, and headed for the main high school, twenty blocks away where I would be going in a week. Pumping slowly, I wondered about the debating team and the other things Mr. Everett had mentioned.

from *Pocho*

José Antonio Villarreal

I

As the months went by, Richard was quieter, sadder, and, at times, even morose. He was aware that the family was undergoing a strange metamorphosis. The heretofore gradual assimilation of this new culture was becoming more pronounced. Along with a new prosperity, the Rubio family was taking on the mores of the middle class, and he did not like it. It saddened him to see the Mexican tradition begin to disappear. And because human nature is such, he, too, succumbed, and unconsciously became an active leader in the change.

"Silence!" roared Juan Rubio. "We will not speak the dog language in my house!" They were at the supper table.

"But this is America, Father," said Richard. "If we live in this country, we must live like Americans."

"And next you will tell me that those are not tortillas you are eating but bread, and those are not beans but *hahm an' ecks.*"

"No, but I mean that you must remember that we are not in México. In México——"

"*Hahm an' ecks,*" his father interrupted. "You know, when I was in Los Angeles for the first time, before your mother found me, all I could say in the English was *hahm an' ecks,* and I ate all my meals in a restaurant. Remember! What makes you think I have to remember that I am not in México? Why . . ."

"You were in the restaurant, Papá."

"Yes, well. . . . Every morning, when the woman came for my order, I would say *hahm an' ecks,* at noon *hahm an' ecks,* at night *hahm an' ecks.* I tell you I was tired, and then, one day, she did not ask, and brought me some soup and some meat. I do not know whether she felt sorry for me or whether they ran out of eggs, but I certainly was happy for the change."

"You are laughing at us," said Richard. "You yourself

[88]

told me there are many Mexican restaurants in Los Angeles."

"Well, I was living in Hollywood at the time, working as an extra in the cowboy movies. There were no Mexicans to speak of in Hollywood." And he would smile in spite of himself, and the children would laugh.

"My teacher says we are all Americans," said one of the girls, who was in the first grade. She stood and began to recite, in a monotone, "I pledge allegiance to the flag—"

"You! Sit down!" said the father, in a loud voice, and laughed. "You are an American with that black face? Just because your name is Rubio does not mean you are really blond."

"It does not matter," said the little girl. "She told us we are all Americans, and she knows. After all, she is a teacher."

But all such scenes did not end with laughter, for Richard's mother was a different person altogether now, and constantly interfered when her husband was in the act of disciplining a child, and these interferences grew until they flared into violent quarrels. And Richard did not like himself, because he knew that many times he caused the disruption of family peace by playing one parent against the other in order to have his way. His mother now took to gossiping and to believing her neighbors, and Juan Rubio, who long ago had decided that he wanted nothing more out of life than to watch his children grow, saw this last vestige of happiness slipping from his grasp, and once more began to have women. Richard knew of it and was ashamed, but did not blame his father, and no longer blamed his mother, because everything was so wrong, and he was to blame as much as anyone else, and no one could do a thing about it.

So he watched the strong man who was his father; watched the raucous, infectious laugh disappear, so that he seldom saw the beautiful teeth again; watched the hair as it turned prematurely white, and the body as it lost its solidness and became flabby. Although he loved his mother, Richard realized that a family could not survive when the woman desired to command, and he knew that his mother was like a starving child who had become gluttonous when confronted with food. She had lived so long in the tradition of her country that she could not help herself now, and abused the privilege of equality afforded the women of her new country. She was not gay now; there was no gayness in her belief that her son was her world, and she proclaimed aloud that she lived only for her boy. For her, there were no songs left.

One day, Juan Rubio cooked his own breakfast, and soon after he moved into another room. Now there was no semblance of discipline whatever, and even the smallest child screamed at either parent, and came and went as she pleased. The house was unkempt and the father complained, but Consuelo, who had always been proud of her talents for housekeeping, now took the dirty house as a symbol of her emancipation, and it was to remain that way until her death.

That day, Richard saw clearly what he had helped create, and sought to repair the damage, but it was too late. What was done was beyond repair. To be just, no one could be blamed, for the transition from the culture of the old world to that of the new should never have been attempted in one generation.

II

Had Juan Rubio been faced with the problem of explaining to himself what had caused the imminent disintegration of his family, he would have been unable to do it. He was not a man to blame outside causes for his misfortunes. To him, life was to be lived, and if in its course things went badly—why, that was life, and he must act to make it as good a life as possible. He believed in God, and vaguely he believed in Heaven, but could not relate the attainment of Heaven to his actions on earth. Immortality was guaranteed under his belief in God, and, as for temporal life, it was enough that he maintain his dignity as a man, that he be true to himself, that he satisfy his body of its needs—and his body needed more than tortillas.

It was in this way, then, after having bought a home for his family and after seeing that his household was breaking up in actuality and that it was not merely a possibility, that he called for the first time at the house of adobe he had helped build in Milpitas. It was midmorning on a sunny day when he knocked on the door, and Macedonia, the wife of his friend Cirilo, opened the door and looked at him impassively.

"I wondered how long it would take you to come," she said, and he noted the resignation in her voice. But this will change, he thought. She cannot remain with this attitude after today. "How long will he be gone?" he asked, making the cuckold-to-be as impersonal as possible, for the mention of his name might be enough to make her change her mind at this delicate point in their relationship.

"Long enough," she said. He followed her into another room.

Thus it was done, and for him there could be no going back. He had returned to former custom, and he would never be weak again, nor would he compromise another time.

III

Richard walked down the street toward his old neighborhood. Though his new home was but a few blocks away, he seldom went near the old place, but on this afternoon he wanted to see Zelda, and he could not approach her anywhere else. He was excited with anticipation, and so engrossed in the pleasant thought of the girl's body that he was startled to hear his name called. He looked up to find that he was in front of the Madison home.

"Come in, Richard," said Mary. "I have something to tell you."

He opened the gate and walked up to the porch. Although they had spent many hours talking together, this was the first time he had been in her yard in the four years of their friendship. He sat on the steps and took a piece of candy she offered him.

"Fudge," she said. "I made it." After a pause, she added, "We're going away to Chicago. Daddy got a job there and we're leaving this week to meet him."

"Well, at least you get to travel," he said lightly, but was surprised to find that the thought of her leaving was saddening. She had been a good friend to him, and the only one of his acquaintances with whom he could talk about some of the things that interested him, now that Joe Pete Manõel was gone. This despite the fact that she was a girl and was younger than he.

She looked at him. "You know what, Richard? I wish Daddy would come back here. I don't want to leave."

"Why? Silly! You'll see a lot of new places and meet a

lot of people. I wouldn't give up a chance like that for anything." This is true, he thought. I am a little jealous of
her.

"I wasn't going to tell you until we grew up, but since
I'm going away, I'll tell you now." She was very frank and
unembarrassed in her seriousness. "I'm going to marry you,
Richard."

"Holy Christ!" he exclaimed in surprise. "Just like that,
huh?" He snapped his fingers.

"No, not just like that. I knew it a long time ago, the
first time I went to your house. Don't laugh at me, Richard,
and please don't swear."

"I'm sorry. I forgot," he apologized. He had trained
himself never to swear in her presence. He felt years older
than she but he knew her moods and the intense way she
had of treating anything in which she believed. He also
knew her temper and the strange effect her outbursts of
anger had on him. So he spoke in an older-brother tone
of voice, yet was careful not to offend her by appearing to
be patronizing. "You read too many romances, Mayrie.
And anyway you were sore at me the first time I took you
to my house, remember?"

"You didn't take me that first time. I went. You were
ashamed to be seen with me."

"You're only a little girl."

"I'm not little. I'm twelve, and you're not fifteen yet, so
that makes it just right."

Her mind was really made up, so he teased her. "But
what if you're ugly when you grow up?"

"That won't matter. I'm still the smartest Goddamn girl
around."

"Hey, wait a minute," he said laughingly. "Now who's
swearing?"

"I'm only saying what you told me," she said.

"You remember everything, don't you? It's a good thing
you're going away, 'cause if you weren't, I don't know how
I'd get you out of my hair."

"You never will," she said, and her self-assurance made
her voice matter-of-fact. "I'll write to you, and you're going
to answer. When it's time, I'll tell you to come for me."
Her words startled Richard so that he felt they were both
thirty years old.

"Okay, Mayrie. I'll write to you," he said, and he found
he was beginning to believe her words.

"You remember that first book you loaned me, Richard? The one about the circus?"

"Yeah?"

"I cried when the monkey was shot," she said.

"That's all right," he said. "I cried every time I read it, too." He stood up. "I've got to go now, Mayrie. I'll be waiting for your letter, and I won't forget." He was already beginning to feel the loss her departure would be. "I'm going to miss you, Mayrie."

"It won't be too long, Richard." She looked down at her feet. "You can kiss me goodbye if you want to."

He leaned down and pressed his lips to hers, and wondered why he did not feel like a Goddamn fool. Jesus, he thought, a little kid like that! He turned once, but she was gone, and he walked slowly, a warmth rising in his chest making him feel a pleasure of just living. What had occurred was really a beautiful thing. Then, he walked rapidly, not looking back any more, though he wanted to do so, until he reached a group of boys playing stickinthemud on the corner.

"Hi," he said. "Zelda around?"

"Nah," said Ricky. "She don't come out much in the afternoons any more."

"What's the matter, you hard up?" asked Ronnie.

Richard looked at him contemptuously. "Why don't you shut up?" he said.

"You can see her tonight if you wanna," said Thomas. "She'll be out to play after supper."

"I guess I'll be around," said Richard. "Well, I'll see you guys after."

"Stick around," said Ricky. "You can eat at my place, so you don't have to go all the way home and back."

"Okay," Richard said, "but your old lady is gonna spaghetti me to death. Jesus, doesn't she ever cook anything else?"

"Sometimes," answered Ricky, then added, with a straight face, "We'll probably have snails tonight."

"I wouldn't doubt it," said Thomas, "you wops'll eat anything." They all laughed at the Japanese boy's remark.

"We're going to Chicago," said Ronnie proudly.

"I hope you freeze your ass off," said Richard. He suddenly realized how very much he disliked Mary's brother. "You know, I'm sorry to see Mary go, but I'm sure glad you're finally getting the hell out of here."

"What do you mean, you're sorry Mary's leaving?" demanded Ronnie.

"She's a good little kid, and I like her," said Richard.

"Listen, if you been fooling around with my sister, I'll—"

"Don't be stupid," said Richard. "She's not like you. She's got twice the brains you got."

"Just keep away from her," said Ronnie belligerently. "I'm glad we're moving away, 'cause I was getting tired of you sucking around her all the time. Calling her Mayrie, and all that. Mother never liked it, either, you know."

"Your old lady's full of what makes green grass grow, just like you are!" said Richard cruelly.

"You can't talk about my mother like that," screamed Ronnie. "Take it back! Take it back!"

"Balls!"

"Take it back, now—or I'll kick the hell out of you!"

"Oh, yeah?"

"Yeah!"

"Yeah!"

"Yeah!"

"You guys gonna yeah all day?" asked Thomas.

"Lay off, Ronnie," said Ricky. Since Zelda's fall, he was the boss.

Ronnie did not want trouble with Ricky, but he said doggedly, "Tell him to take it back!"

"Aw, shut up!" said Ricky. "Come on, Richard. Let's go eat those snails." The two boys moved off, and Ronnie said:

"My mother's right about this lousy town. No decent people at all—just a bunch of Mexicans and Japs and I don't know what kind of crud!"

Thomas hit him on the mouth, and Ronnie sat down and began to cry. They left him there.

Thomas said, "Let's go uptown, you guys, and I'll blow ya to a milkshake." They laughed at him. "Hones'. I got money. I fought a guy in Watsonville last night." They turned around and went in the opposite direction. Thomas could never be angry very long.

"Hey, Richard, how come you always picking on Ronnie? What you got against him, huh, anyhow?"

"I just can't go the sucker! You know how I hate to fight, but if he wasn't Mary's brother, I would have taken him a long time ago."

"Aw, he's all right. Just got the bighead, that's all," said Ricky. "Hey," he asked as an afterthought, "you ain't been fooling around that little kid, have you? Honest?"

"That's San Quentin quail," said Thomas, attempting to sound like a man of the world.

"Who, Mary?" Richard laughed. "Hell, no." Then, for no apparent reason, he said, "She wants to marry me." He squirmed uneasily.

"That would really fix Ronnie's water, wouldn't it?" Ricky said, laughing. Ricky could be real good sometimes.

They had their milkshake, and then returned to Ricky's house, where his father let them have a glass of Dago-red. They walked along feeling very warm inside.

"Let's go out to Bracher's orchard," said Richard.

"Jeez," said Ricky. "One thing I don't like about you is you always want to walk someplace. I musta walked about a hundred miles with you already. It wouldn't be so bad if you at least talked to me, but once you get me out in those caboulders, you don't say a word."

"You're coming, too, aren't you, Thomas?"

"Not me. I live in a berry patch, remember? I'll wait here for you guys."

"Aw, come on," said Ricky. "Maybe we can cop some cherries."

It was nighttime by the time they returned from their walk, and a game of hideandgoseek was in progress. They had long ago outgrown such games, but there seemed nothing else to do, and Zelda was playing. As they ran to hide, Richard followed her. She chose as her hiding place an indentation in the earth about two feet deep, which had been made by the removal of an old oak stump. The grass was tall, and it was dark in the empty lot.

"Get the hell away from here," she said. "This is my place!"

"I'm hiding here, too," he said.

"I'm warnin' ya," said Zelda. "Beat it!"

When he tried to get down into the hole with her, they began to fight. For fully five minutes, they struggled in the darkness. Suddenly she began to cry. It was the first time he had heard her cry when she was not in a rage. And he understood the reason for her tears. It was the end of an era for her; her dominance was over, and her life would be a different one from now on. One of her eyes was badly bruised, and her mouth was bleeding.

"Ya hurt my tit," she said, and held her left breast.

"Let me rub it," he said. "You might get cancer."

"What's that?"

"It's a sickness. If you get it, they'll hafta cut it off."

"Jesus!" she said, and was frightened. He opened her shirt and stroked her breast. She stared at him wide-eyed. Then he was tasting the blood in her mouth, and as they sank down together, he could hear the boy who was "it" chanting, "Five, ten, fifteen, twenty . . ."

When it was over, she said, "That was different, Richard."

"I know." He was lying on his back, staring at the sky. She rolled over, so that the upper part of her body was on his chest, and gently ran both hands across his forehead and down over his hair. She was enchanted that she could get such pleasure from doing that. She kissed him lightly. "You're the first guy I ever kissed," she said. Then, "I guess I love ya, Richard."

Jeez, he thought. Twice on the same day! He felt extremely good. "You're my girl now," he said. "You're going to have to be different from now on. No more overhauls, and you're going to hafta stop laying pipe with all the guys."

"Yes, Richard." She was full of happiness in her new role, and for the first time in her young life she was glad to be a woman.

"And you hafta quit all that swearing and fighting."

"Yes, Richard." They were quiet for a moment. Then she asked, "Why'd ya do it, Richard?"

"Why'd I do what?"

"Why'd ya make me do it with all the guys that day?"

"I don't know," he said. "I didn't care about them, but I wanted it, and that was the only way I could get it."

She thought back for a while. "I guess I musta felt this way about ya for a long time, and didn't know it even, 'cause when you told me my legs was dirty that day, I wanted to say something mean, but instead I was ashamed. I'm sorry I called ya all those names, Richard."

"That's all right. Names never hurt me."

"And I know you probably don't like to talk about it— about the guys an' up in the haylof' an' all that. I just wantcha ta know that I never did it when you weren't around. I don't know why, I just never did."

"That's not what Ricky and Ronnie say."

"I don't care, they're big liars." She was quietly angry for a moment, and then afraid that her past conduct would alienate him. "You believe me, don'tcha, Richard? You gotta believe me, because I can't be your girl if you don't."

"Sure I believe you," he said. Somehow it mattered very much to him that he should believe her, and he never thought he could be like that. "They're just jealous," he said, and he knew that in a way they really were.

Zelda kept her face averted, her head on his chest now, and was holding him tight. She knew instinctively that every possible complication must be brought out. She asked, "Richard, do you like Mary?"

"Whaddaya mean?"

She was embarrassed. "Well, everybody knows that you're with her a lot."

"She's just one of my best friends, that's all. They're moving away this week."

"I'm glad," she said. "I'm afraid of her."

He laughed but was pleased by her jealousy. "You'll never have to be afraid of Mary," he said.

The new, more drastic change that came over Zelda was a mystery to the neigborhood. As her speech and manner improved, she became aware that she was more than a little attractive. She worked at being feminine with as much fervor as she had resisted it for so long. Her blond hair, which had not become darker, as usually happens, she had inherited from her Nordic mother, and her Portuguese father had contributed the early maturity, which, combined with years of strenuous exercise, made her at fourteen more a beautiful young woman than a pretty girl. And as she was in high school now, she made new friends and had a large following of boys. They praised her beauty, and she was pleased in spite of her self-consciousness. Because she became friendly to everyone and was accustomed to meeting boys on their own ground, she had trouble, for these new acquaintances did not know what she was like, and misinterpreted her good nature. When confronted by an overenthusiastic pursuer, she reverted to her old defense. She had yet to learn the little artifices girls use to keep insistent boys at bay yet friendly. So she resorted to her fists for protection, and when she violently spurned their advances, the boys thought of her as a teaser, and this troubled her, because she considered that the worst thing a woman could be.

Her relationship with Richard ripened into a deep love

on her part and an indifferent one on his. It was understood between them that they would someday marry, and
although he never told her he loved her, she was satisfied
with the knowledge that she was his girl. She responded to
his newfound and now everpresent dominance, and made
token resistance to his whims only because it pleased him
that she occasionally showed spirit. Yet she knew that she
would have obeyed his every wish without a whimper. Her
only fear was of pregnancy, because she knew he would
leave her if that happened; he would never consent to a ·
marriage when the reason was anything other than the
desire to be with a woman for life. She loved his sensitivity and the gentleness he showed her, for she had never
had such attention or encouraged it, but she was aware
that he was capable of great cruelty. Only her closeness
to him enabled her to see that part of his character, and
she was the first to recognize it. Richard himself was not
yet objective enough to discover this fault in his makeup.

He visited her home when her parents and brothers
were out, and sometimes they walked out of town in the
evenings. The Catholic cemetery became a favorite place
for their nocturnal trysts, but they were much happier
when he could borrow a car and they drove far enough
away so they weren't afraid of being caught. He would
spread a blanket on the ground, and they would lie for
hours under the stars. Their naked bodies in the wan light
contrasted sharply; her whiteness paled and his brownness
became swarthier. Their minds, at times like this, were
free of the worry of detection, and thus, at their ease, their
play and lovemaking was a thing of infinite beauty to both
of them.

Few people knew that Zelda was his girl, because Richard
seldom took her to the movies or to dances. Nor did they
spend all their time together, as most young people going
steady will do. She, for the most part, stayed home, learning
the many things of housewifery she had neglected all her
life. She did not have girl friends, because she had never
associated with girls and now found their talk silly and bor-
ing, so she strove instead to become interested in the things
Richard liked. She thought reading was laborious and painful, but persevered and found enjoyment. She worked pain-
stakingly on her schoolwork, because he scolded her about
her grades and she did not want him to feel ashamed of her.
And though she always knew when he became interested in

another girl, she never questioned him, because in her heart she was sure of him, and they always managed to be together at least three times a week. They never tired of each other's young virility.

In this new routine, Richard lost part of the restlessness that had tortured him for so long. He still felt the need for that unknown; that substantiality that had eluded men from the beginning of time, but it lost its importance for the present. He was young, and the time for the pursuit of the esoteric would come soon enough. When the day came that he married Zelda, he would be forced to find himself, for Richard was certain that he could never revolve his whole life around marriage. He could not give that institution the importance it had falsely taken on through the centuries. Marriage, per se, was not life, nor could it govern life.

In this he believed.

IV

Richard Rubio, lost in thought, walked slowly into his front yard. He was relaxed, although his body was bruised and sore from football practice. They had scrimmaged that day, for there was a game on Friday, and although there was little chance that he, as a scrub, would get into the game at all, he played as much during practice as the first string did. It was with the reserves that the regulars conditioned themselves and perfected their timing. Richard had almost quit when he realized that he would never make the first team, but upon reflection he knew that he enjoyed the contact and that the practice sessions took up a great deal of his time, of which there was too much for him at the moment.

The Rubio front yard was a large one, and Juan Rubio had planted a vegetable garden. There were tomatoes there now, and chiles. The driveway and the back yard, where there was another garden, were neat and orderly. At the extreme end of the property was a chicken coop, newly whitewashed, and rabbit hutches.

He reached the end of the driveway and stepped onto the porch. Then he noticed that his sister Luz sat in a car in front of the house, talking to a boy from school whom he vaguely knew. Inside the house, he was suddenly filled with sorrow mingled with disgust, as he always was these days when he came home. Trash and garbage were on the floor;

bedrooms were unkempt, with beds unmade. On the floor of the living room, where two of the girls slept, blankets and a mat still lay, reeking strongly of urine, because the girls still wet their beds at the ages of eight and ten. Only his bed was made up, because his mother could not neglect him. His clothes were pressed and in order in his closet, but elsewhere he saw a slip here, a brassière there; odds and ends of clothing lay wherever the wearer decided to undress. In the kitchen, the sink was full of dishes, dirty water nearly overflowing onto the littered floor. The stove was caked with grease, its burners barely allowing enough gas to permit a flame to live.

He threw his books on his bed, then went to his mother and kissed her. She sat with one of his younger sisters between her legs, going through her hair with a fine comb. A louse cracked loudly between her thumbnails.

"Go!" he said to the little girl. "Go and bring my sisters here—and Luz, too."

"But her head smells of coal oil," protested his mother. "She cannot go out among her neighbors smelling like that."

He was angry and impatient, and his voice was harsh. "Do you think that because our house is so filthy, we are the only ones in Santa Clara who have lice?" He turned to his little sister again and said, "Go!" She jumped to her feet and ran out the door.

The girls came into the house one by one. There was a frightened look in their faces, and they immediately began to clean the house. They knew what he wanted, for this was not the first time this had happened.

"Where is Luz?" he demanded.

"She won't come in," said one of the girls. "She said to tell you to go to hell."

He walked to the car very quickly, in a rage he had never known himself capable of feeling. He said calmly, however, and in Spanish, "Go inside and help your sisters, big lazy."

"Don't bother me," she answered.

"What does he want?" asked the boy, from behind the wheel.

"He don't want me to be out here with you," she lied.

"Go take a shit," said the boy to Richard.

Richard opened the door and pulled her out onto the sidewalk. He slapped her hard twice, and she ran into the house screaming. The boy got out of his car, and he was big, powerful. Richard backed away toward the yard next door and took a brick from an abandoned incinerator.

"Come on, you big son of a bitch," he said. "Come after me and I'll kill you!" The boy hesitated, then moved forward again. "That's it," said Richard, "come on and get your Goddamn head busted wide open."

The boy went back to his car. "You're crazy!" he shouted. "Crazier'n hell!"

That night, for the first time in months, they had dinner together in the old way. After dinner, his father sat on the rocker in the living room, listening to the Mexican station from Piedras Negras on short wave. When the kitchen was picked up, the girls sat around restlessly in the living room, and Richard knew they wanted to listen to something else, so he said to his father, "Let us go into the kitchen. I have a new novel in the Spanish I will read to you."

In the kitchen, around the table, his mother also sat down, and said, "It is a long time, little son, that you do not read to us."

How blind she must be, he thought. Aloud he said, "It is called *Crime and Punishment*, and it is about the Rusos in another time." He read rapidly and they listened attentively, interrupting him only now and then with a surprised "Oh!" or "That is so true!" After two hours, he could not read fast enough for himself, and he wished he could read all night to them, because it was a certainty that he would not get another opportunity to read to them like this. They would never get to know the book, and he knew they were to miss something great. He knew also that they would never be this close together again. How he knew this he could not even guess, and that was sad in itself, besides their having to do without the book.

"There are new Mexican people in town, Papá," he said. "In school today, there were two boys and a girl."

"Yes, I know," said Juan Rubio. "Every year, more and more of us decide to remain here in the valley."

"They are funny," said Luz, who, along with two or three of the girls, had come into the kitchen.

"They dress strangely," said Richard.

"In San Jose," said Juan Rubio, "on Saturday night during the summer, I have seen these youngsters in clown costumes. It is the fashion of Los Angeles."

"They are different from us," said Luz. "Even in their features they are different from us."

"They come from a different part of México, that is all," said Consuelo, who knew of such things, for she herself was different from all of them, except for her son, and this because her great-grandfather had come from Yucatán.

"Well, at any rate, they are a coarse people," said Luz.

Richard and his father exchanged looks and laughed. She flushed in anger, and said in English to Richard, "Well, they ain't got nuthin' and they don't even talk good English."

He laughed louder, and his father laughed even though he did not know what she had said.

It was not until the following year that Richard knew that his town was changing as much as his family was. It was 1940 in Santa Clara, and, among other things, the Conscription Act had done its part in bringing about a change. It was not unusual now to see soldiers walking downtown or to see someone of the town in uniform. He was aware that people liked soldiers now, and could still remember the old days, when a detachment of cavalry camped outside the town for a few days or a unit of field artillery stayed at the university, and the worst thing one's sister could do was associate with a soldier. Soldiers were common, were drunkards, thieves, and rapers of girls, or something, to the people of Santa Clara, and the only uniforms with prestige in the town had been those of the CCC boys or of the American Legion during the Fourth of July celebration and the Easter-egg hunt. But now everybody loved a soldier, and he wondered how this had come about.

There were the soldiers, and there were also the Mexicans in ever-increasing numbers. The Mexican people Richard had known until now were those he saw only during the summer, and they were migrant families who seldom remained in Santa Clara longer than a month or two. The orbit of his existence was limited to the town, and actually to his immediate neighborhood, thereby preventing his association with the Mexican family which lived on the other side of town, across the tracks. In his wanderings into San Jose, he began to see more of what he called "the race." Many of the migrant workers who came up from southern California in the late spring and early summer now settled down in the valley. They bought two hundred pounds of flour and a hundred pounds of beans, and if they weathered the first winter, which was the most difficult, because the rains stopped agricultural workers from earning a living, they were settled for good.

As the Mexican population increased, Richard began to attend their dances and fiestas, and, in general, sought their company as much as possible, for these people were a strange lot to him. He was obsessed with a hunger to learn about them and from them. They had a burning contempt for people of different ancestry, whom they called Americans, and a marked hauteur toward México and toward their parents for their old-country ways. The former feeling came from a sense of inferiority that is a prominent characteristic in any Mexican reared in southern California; and the latter was an inexplicable compensation for that feeling. They needed to feel superior to something, which is a natural thing. The result was that they attempted to segregate themselves from both their cultures, and became truly a lost race. In their frantic desire to become different, they adopted a new mode of dress, a new manner, and even a new language. They used a polyglot speech made up of English and Spanish syllables, words, and sounds. This they incorporated into phrases and words that were unintelligible to anyone but themselves. Their Spanish became limited and their English more so. Their dress was unique to the point of being ludicrous. The black motif was predominant. The tight-fitting cuffs on trouserlegs that billowed at the knees made Richard think of some longforgotten pasha in the faraway past, and the fingertip coat and highly lustrous shoes gave the wearer, when walking, the appearance of a strutting cock. Their hair was long and swept up to meet in the back, forming a ducktail. They spent hours training it to remain that way.

The girls were characterized by the extreme shortness of their skirts, which stopped well above the knees. Their jackets, too, were fingertip in length, coming to within an inch of the skirt hem. Their hair reached below the shoulder in the back, and it was usually worn piled in front to form a huge pompadour.

The pachuco was born in El Paso, had gone west to Los Angeles, and was now moving north. To society, these zootsuiters were a menace, and the name alone classified them as undesirables, but Richard learned that there was much more to it than a mere group with a name. That in spite of their behavior, which was sensational at times and violent at others, they were simply a portion of a confused humanity, employing their self-segregation as a means of expression. And because theirs was a spontaneous, and not a planned, retaliation, he saw it as a vicissitude of society, obviously only because of its nature and comparative suddenness.

From the leggy, short-skirted girls, he learned that their mores were no different from those of what he considered good girls. What was under the scant covering was as inaccessible as it would be under the more conventional dress. He felt, in fact, that these girls were more difficult to reach. And from the boys he learned that their bitterness and hostile attitude toward "whites" was not merely a lark. They had learned hate through actual experience, with everything the word implied. They had not been as lucky as he, and showed the scars to prove it. And, later on, Richard saw in retrospect that what happened to him in the city jail in San Jose was due more to the character of a handful of men than to the wide, almost organized attitude of a society, for just as the zootsuiters were blamed en masse for the action of a few, they in turn, blamed the other side for the very same reason.

As happens in most such groups, there were misunderstandings and disagreements over trivia. Pachucos fought among themselves, for the most part, and they fought hard. It was not unusual that a quarrel born on the streets or backalleys of a Los Angeles slum was settled in the Santa Clara Valley. Richard understood them and partly sympathized, but their way of life was not entirely justified in his mind, for he felt that they were somehow reneging on life; this was the easiest thing for them to do. They, like his father, were defeated—only more so, because they really never started to live. They, too, were but making a show of resistance.

Of the new friends Richard made, those who were native to San Jose were relegated to become casual acquaintances, for they were as Americanized as he, and did not interest him. The newcomers became the object of his explorations. He was avidly hungry to learn the ways of these people. It was not easy for him to approach them at first, because his clothes labeled him as an outsider, and, too, he had trouble understanding their speech. He must not ask quiestions, for fear of offending them; his deductions as to their character and makeup must come from close association. He was careful not to be patronizing or in any way act superior. And, most important, they must never suspect what he was doing. The most difficult moments for him were when he was doing the talking, for he was conscious that his Spanish was better than theirs. He learned enough of their vernacular to get along; he did not learn more, because he was always in a hurry about knowledge. Soon he counted a few boys as friends, but had a much harder time of it with the girls, because they considered him a traitor to his "race." Before he knew it, he found that he almost never spoke to them in English, and no longer defended the "whites," but, rather, spoke disparagingly of them whenever possible. He also bought a suit to wear when in their company, not with such an extreme cut as those they wore, but removed enough from the conservative so he would not be considered a square. And he found himself a girl, who refused to dance the faster pieces with him, because he still jittered in the American manner. So they danced only to soft music while they kissed in the dimmed light, and that was the extent of their lovemaking. Or he stood behind her at the bar, with his arms around her as she sipped a Nehi, and felt strange because she was a Mexican and everyone around them was also Mexican, and felt stranger still from the knowledge that he felt strange. When the dance was over, he took her where her parents were sitting and said goodnight to the entire family.

Whenever his new friends saw him in the company of his school acquaintances, they were courteously polite, but they later chastised him for fraternizing with what they called the enemy. Then Richard had misgivings, because he knew that his desire to become one of them was not a sincere one in that respect, yet upon reflection he realized that in truth he enjoyed their company and valued their friendship, and his sense of guilt was gone. He went along with everything they did, being careful only to keep away from serious trouble with no loss of prestige. Twice he entered the dreamworld induced by marihuana, and after the effect of the drug was expended, he was surprised to discover that he did not crave it, and was glad, for he could not afford a kick like that. As it was, life was too short for him to be able to do the many things he knew he still must do. The youths understood that he did not want it, and never pressed him.

Now the time came to withdraw a little. He thought it

would be a painful thing, but they liked him, and their friendliness made everything natural. He, in his gratefulness, loved them for it.

I can be a part of everything, he thought, because I am the only one capable of controlling my destiny. . . . Never —no, never—will I allow myself to become a part of a group—to become classified, to lose my individuality. . . . I will not become a follower, nor will I allow myself to become a leader, because I must be myself and accept for myself only that which I value, and not what is being valued by everyone else these days . . . like a Goddamn suit of clothes they're wearing this season or Cuban heels . . . a style in ethics. What shall we do to liven up the season this year of Our Lord 1940, you from the North, and you from the South, and you from the East, and you from the West? Be original, and for Chrissake speak up! Shall we make it a vogue to sacrifice virgins—but, no, that's been done. . . . What do you think of matricide or motherrape? No? Well— wish we could deal with more personal things, such as prolonging the gestation period in the Homo sapiens; that would keep the married men hopping, no?

He thought this and other things, because the young are like that, and for them nothing is impossible; no, nothing is impossible, and this truism gives impetus to the impulse to laugh at abstract bonds. This night he thought this, and could laugh at the simplicity with which he could render powerless obstacles in his search for life, he had returned to the Mexican dancehall for the first time in weeks, and the dance was fast coming to a close. The orchestra had blared out a jazzedup version of "Home, Sweet Home" and was going through it again at a much slower tempo, giving the couples on the dancefloor one last chance for the sensual embraces that would have to last them a week. Richard was dancing with his girl, leading with his leg and holding her slight body close against his, when one of his friends tapped him on the shoulder.

"We need some help," he said. "Will you meet us by the door after the dance?" The question was more of a command, and the speaker did not wait for an answer. The dance was over, and Richard kissed the girl goodbye and joined the group that was gathering conspicuously as the people poured out through the only exit.

"What goes?" he asked.

"We're going to get some guys tonight," answered the

youth who had spoken to him earlier. He was twenty years old and was called the Rooster.

The Mexican people have an affinity for incongruous nicknames. In this group, there was Tuerto, who was not blind; Cacarizo, who was not pockmarked; Zurdo, who was not left-handed; and a drab little fellow who was called Slick. Only Chango was appropriately named. There was indeed something anthropoidal about him.

The Rooster said, "They beat hell out of my brother last night, because he was jiving with one of their girls. I just got the word that they'll be around tonight if we want trouble."

"Man," said Chango, "we want a mess of trouble."

"Know who they are?" asked the Tuerto.

"Yeah. It was those bastards from Ontario," said the Rooster. "We had trouble with them before."

"Where they going to be?" asked Richard.

"That's what makes it good. Man, it's going to be real good," said the Rooster. "In the Orchard. No cops, no nothing. Only us."

"And the mud," said the Tuerto. The Orchard was a twelve-acre cherry grove in the new industrial district on the north side of the city.

"It'll be just as muddy for them," said the Rooster. "Let's go!"

They walked out and hurriedly got into the car. There were eight of them in Zurdo's sedan, and another three were to follow in a coupé. Richard sat in the back on Slick's lap. He was silent, afraid that they might discover the growing terror inside him. The Rooster took objects out of a gunnysack.

"Here, man, this is for you. Don't lose it," he said. It was a doubledup bicycle chain, one end bound tightly with leather thongs to form a grip.

Richard held it in his hands and, for an unaccountable reason, said, "Thank you." Goddamn! he thought. What the hell did I get into? He wished they would get to their destination quickly, before his fear turned to panic. He had no idea who it was they were going to meet. Would there be three or thirty against them? He looked at the bludgeon in his hand and thought, Christ! Somebody could get killed!

The Tuerto passed a pint of whiskey back to them. Richard drank thirstily, then passed the bottle on.

"You want some, Chango?" asked the Rooster.

"That stuff's not for me, man. I stick to yesca," he answered. Four jerky rasps came from him as he inhaled, reluctant to allow the least bit of smoke to escape him, receiving the full force of the drug in a hurry. He offered the cigarette, but they all refused it. Then he carefully put it out, and placed the butt in a small matchbox.

It seemed to Richard that they had been riding for hours when finally they arrived at the Orchard. They backed the car under the trees, leaving the motor idling because they might have to leave in a hurry. The rest of the gang did not arrive; the Rooster said, "Those sons of bitches aren't coming!"

"Let's wait a few minutes," said the Tuerto. "Maybe they'll show up."

"No, they won't come," said the Rooster, in a calm voice now. He unzipped his pants legs and rolled them up to the knees. "Goddamn mud," he said, almost good-naturedly. "Come on!" They followed him into the Orchard. When they were approximately in the center of the tract, they stopped. "Here they come," whispered the Rooster.

Richard could not hear a thing. He was more afraid, but had stopped shaking. In spite of his fear, his mind was alert. He strained every sense, in order not to miss any part of this experience. He wanted to retain everything that was about to happen. He was surprised at the way the Rooster had taken command from the moment they left the dancehall. Richard had never thought of any one of the boys being considered a leader, and now they were all following the Rooster, and Richard fell naturally in line. The guy's like ice, he thought. Like a Goddamn piece of ice!

Suddenly forms took shape in the darkness before him. And just as suddenly he was in the kaleidoscopic swirl of the fight. He felt blows on his face and body, as if from a distance, and he flayed viciously with the chain. There was a deadly quietness to the struggle. He was conscious that some of the fallen were moaning, and a voice screamed, "The son of a bitch broke my arm!" And that was all he heard for a while, because he was lying on the ground with his face in the mud.

They halfdragged, halfcarried him to the car. It had bogged down in the mud, and they put him in the back while they tried to make it move. They could see headlights behind them, beyond the trees.

"We have to get the hell out of here," said the Rooster.

"They got help. Push! Push!" Richard opened the door and fell out of the car. He got up and stumbled crazily in the darkness. He was grabbed and violently thrown in again. They could hear the sound of a large group coming toward them from the Orchard.

"Let's cut out!" shouted the Tuerto. "Leave it here!"

"No!" said the Rooster. "They'll tear it apart!" The car slithered onto the sidewalk and the wheels finally got traction. In a moment, they were moving down the street.

Richard held his hands to his head. "Jesus!" he exclaimed. "The cabrón threw me with the shithouse."

"It was a bat," said the Rooster.

"What?"

"He hit you with a Goddamn baseball bat!"

They took Richard home, and the Rooster helped him to his door. "Better rub some lard on your head," he told him.

"All right. Say, you were right, Rooster. Those other cats didn't show at all."

"You have to expect at least a couple of guys to chicken out on a deal like this," said the Rooster. "You did real good, man. I knew you'd do good."

Richard looked at his friend thoughtfully for a moment. In the dim light, his dark hair, Medusa-like, curled from his collar in back almost his eyebrows. He wondered what errant knight from Castile had traveled four thousand miles to mate with a daughter of Cuahtémoc to produce this strain. "How did you know?" he asked.

"Because I could tell it meant so much to you," said the Rooster.

"When I saw them coming, it looked like there were a hundred of them."

"There were only about fifteen. You're okay, Richard. Any time you want something, just let me know."

Richard felt humble in his gratification. He understood the friendship that was being offered. "I'll tell you, Rooster," he said. "I've never been afraid as much as I was tonight." He thought, If he knows this, perhaps he won't feel the sense of obligation.

"Hell, that's no news. We all were."

"Did we beat them?" asked Richard.

"Yeah, we beat them," answered the Rooster. "We beat them real good!"

And that, for Richard Rubio, was the finest moment of a most happy night.

V

And yet oddly, despite the chances he took, it was while in the company of his childhood friends that Richard became involved with the police. It happened so suddenly that he had no chance to prepare himself for the experience.

Ricky had a car now, and the gang was going to get him skirts for it as a sort of a present. They searched all over San Jose until they found a car with a set that would look good on Ricky's, but they had not even started to take them off when two night watchmen, on their way home from work somewhere, stopped them. The men really had nothing to hold them on, because they had not done anything yet, but Richard knew they did not need a reason.

The guards had them lined up against the firehouse when the squadcars arrived. The lead car had not yet come to a complete stop when the rear door opened and the first cop jumped out. He kept moving toward them in one motion, and as Richard was the closest to him, he got it first, in the face, and the back of his head hit the brick wall and he slid down to the sidewalk. The guys jumped the cop then, crying and swinging, but it was a futile attack, because the rest of the officers were out of the cars by then, and they simply beat them to pieces. They were thrown into the back of the cars bodily, and were lucky they did not hit the side of the car as they went through the door. They were hit and jabbed in the ribs all the way to the city jail. The cars went down a ramp into the cellar of the joint, and they were pushed and dragged into a large room. First all their belongings were taken from them and put in individual paper bags, and then a big man in plain clothes came in.

Richard asked where he could lodge a complaint against the officers for beating them, but the detective just grinned.

"Resisting arrest," someone said.

The plainclothesman went into the buddybuddy act with them, and laughed as if the whole thing were a great joke.

"What were you going to do to the car, fellows?" he asked almost jovially.

They did not answer him. One of the cops went over to Ricky and hit him under the ear, and, when he fell, gave him the boots.

"Goddamn pachucos!" he said.

"Now," said the detective, "maybe one of you other guys wants to tell me."

They remained silent, and were all given another beating. Richard's head ached, and he was frightened. He remembered that when he was a kid, a friend of the family had been picked up for drunkenness, and was later found dead in his cell under mysterious circumstances. He realized he must say something—anything.

"We weren't doing anything," he said. "Just fooling around town when those guards hollered at us, and we stopped to see what they wanted."

"How about the girls? Had any idea in mind about the girls?"

"What girls?"

"The two girls walking by—don't make out you don't know what I'm talking about. You Goddamn bastards think you can come here and just take a clean white girl and do what you want! Where you from, anyway? Flats? Boyle Heights?" He really thought they were from Los Angeles.

"We're from Santa Clara and we don't run around raping girls." The detective slapped him with the back of his hand. He looked at him for a minute and said:

"Don't give me that crap. You little bastards give us more trouble than all the criminals in the state. . . . God, I wish we had a free hand to clean out our town of scum like you! Now, you're going to tell me! What were you doing by that car?"

Richard decided to keep silent, like the others, and the detective left the room. Then a cop began taking them one by one. Ricky was halfcarried into the other room, and Richard began to think about how rough it all was. Strange how the police thought they were zootsuiters. Hell, they all had on Levis and wore their hair short.

Ricky was brought back almost immediately, and Richard could see by the stubborn expression on his face that he had not said a word. He could also see that he was frightened, too, but still game as hell. They took one of the others in, but he also came out almost immediately, and the cop motioned to Richard. He knew then that the detective would not waste time with the others, because while they had been silent, he had at least answered some of the questions. But he did not really know what to expect.

"Sit down, kid." The detective's approach was different this time. "Tell me all about it." Richard almost laughed, because now he was being conned; and he suddenly realized that this was the last of it and the detective would not hold them, because he had nothing to keep them on.

"There isn't anything to tell," he said, and the officer made a little joke about how Richard was the only one who would speak up, and how that showed he was not afraid, like the others—though he knew all along it was just the opposite. And Richard knew that he knew this, but now he was over his fear and talked to him calmly, not with the voice he had earlier, when he was near cracking up. The thought of what he must have sounded like shamed him so he damn near puked. "Look, sir," he said. "What are you holding us for, anyway? You want us to tell you we did something we didn't, but I don't know what it is. And then knocking hell out of us like that . . ."

"You resisted arrest."

"Not in here we didn't resist arrest. How come these guys been batting us around like that? You must be a bunch of sadists, all of you. What if one of us dies, or something?"

"I don't know what you're talking about," said the detective. He asked the cop at the door, "You see anyone get hit around here?"

"No. He's crazy," he answered.

"See?" The detective thought he was a real actor. "Now, look. You tell me what you were doing, and I'll see that you get a break."

"Nothing, I told you."

"All right, then, don't tell me about tonight. But how about on other nights? What have you guys been up to? A little stealing, maybe? Where do you get your marihuana? You been maybe jumping a nice little gringa out in Willow Glen? We haven't got the bastard that pulled that one yet!" He stopped, because his anger was becoming obvious in spite of himself. He said casually, "You know about that, don't you?"

"No."

"Well, then, you heard about it."

"No. I haven't."

"You read the papers, no?"

"Only the sports page—the rest of it's a lot of bull and I don't have time for it."

He did not believe him. "You can't tell me that," he said. "You must read the papers sometimes."

"Sure, sometimes I'll glance at the first page, but I don't even do that very much. I just take the second section and read the sports. Maybe when this happened that you're talking about, I didn't look at the front page."

"Hell, no wonder you people are almost illiterate. How you going to know how to vote when you get old enough?"

"I don't want to vote. I just want to get out of here." He was beginning to feel sick, really sick, and his kidneys hurt him so that he was sure he would be passing blood for a week.

"You have to want to vote—it's one right you're guaranteed." He seemed to be a little sorry about that.

"If that's so," said Richard, "then it's my right to not vote if I don't want to vote, isn't it?"

The man dropped it. "This little girl I was telling you about . . . she was walking home from the movies, and three Mexicans pulled her behind a hedge and had some fun."

He seemed to want to keep talking, so Richard asked, "How do you know they were Mexicans?"

"She saw them."

"Yeah, but did she see their birth certificates? Maybe they were Americans?"

The detective looked at him for such a long time that he thought, Oh-oh, I did it this time, but the man had decided a while ago not to use force again. "You're a wise little bastard," he finally said. "Talk pretty good English, too, not like most 'chucos." Again he tried hard not to show his anger, but his voice was loud once more. "You know what I mean when I say Mexican, so don't get so Goddamn smart. She said they were Mexican, that's how we know. Maybe it was your gang."

Richard felt good, because he was certain the detective was going to have to let them go, so he really began to act smart. "We're not a gang," he said. "That is, not a gang the way you mean, only a gang like kids' gangs are, because we grew up together and we played cops-and-robbers, you know. And funny how we used to fight because we all wanted to be the good guys, but now I don't think it was such a good idea, because I just got a pretty good look at the good guys." That jolted the detective a little, and he looked almost embarrassed.

"We have a job to do," he said, explaining everything. "Now, you're sure you guys didn't have anything to do with that?" He said it real cutelike, a sneak punch, and for a moment Richard thought that he would ask where he had been on such-and-such a night, but the detective just smiled his friendly smile.

"I'm sure," Richard said, and smiled right back at him, and one side of his face was so numb that he knew it was not smiling like the other side. "I'm the only Mexican—like *you* say Mexican—in the bunch," he said. "And the others are Spanish, and one is Italian. Besides, I don't know any 'chucos well enough to run around with them."

"Let me see your hands." He looked and was satisfied. "No tattoos. But that's a bad-looking wart you got there."

"I've been playing with frogs," he said sarcastically, but the detective appeared to miss it.

"Better have it taken care of," he said with honest concern. "You still say you don't come from down south?"

"Call up the Santa Clara police, and they'll tell you about me. About all of us."

He was sent into the other room then, and after a while an officer returned their wallets and things and told them they could go. The detective stopped Richard at the door and said:

"So you're going to be a college boy?"

"I guess so." So he *had* checked up.

"Drop in and see me sometime. We can use someone like you when you get older. There are a lot of your people around now, and someone like you would be good to have on the side of law and order."

Jesus Christ! Another one, thought Richard. Aloud he said, "No, thanks. I don't want to have anything to do with you guys."

"Think about it. You have a few years yet. There's a lot you can do for your people that way."

His sincerity surprised Richard. He seemed to mean it. "No," he answered. "I'm no Jesus Christ. Let 'my people' take care of themselves."

"You were defending them a while ago."

"I was defending myself!" *Stupid!*

But who the hell were his people? He had always felt that all people were his people—not in that nauseating God-made-us-all-equal way, for to him that was a deception; the exact opposite was so obvious. But this man, in his attitude and behavior, gave him a new point of view about his world.

Painfully, they walked across town to Ricky's car and somehow made it home. He could not sleep. Things were going on around him that he did not know about. He was amazed at his naïveté. Hearing about Mexican kids being picked up by the police for having done something had never affected him in any way before. Even policemen had never been set aside in his mind as a group. In Santa Clara, where he knew the town marshal and his patrolmen, and always called them by their first names, he did not think of them as cops but as people—in fact, neighbors. One evening had changed all that for him, and now he knew that he would never forget what had happened tonight, and the impression would make him distrust and, in fact, almost hate policemen all his life. Now, for the first time in his life, he felt discriminated against. The horrible thing that he had experienced suddenly was clear, and he cried silently in his bed.

In México they hang the Spaniard, he thought, and here they would do the same to the Mexican, and it was the same person, somehow, doing all this, in another body—in another place. What do they do, these people? That detective, when he is not slapping a face or cajoling or entreating for a confession of some unsolved crime—what does he do when he is not doing this horrible thing he calls a job? Does he have a home, a hearth? A wife upon whom he lavishes all the tenderness in him, whom he holds naked—the only way—to his own nakedness, and in his nakedness is he then real? Or perhaps even—Jesus Christ, NO! NOT CHILDREN! A man like that have children! The wonder of that!

And the guys—they had not said anything, but the way they had looked at him for having stayed in the office so long with that man. "Man," that is truly the worst thing he could possibly call him at this moment. They had been afraid that he had betrayed their trust. Once, on the silent ride home, he had almost exclaimed, "Look, you bastards, I didn't cop out on you. He tried to con me and I conned *him*, and he had to let us go." But he was hurt and a little resentful, and decided they were not worth it. And now they were thinking that if he had not been there, they would not have been accused by association, and therefore not beaten. They were right, of course. And, in a way he had betrayed them, but they did not know this. He had kept his mouth shut, not because of the code but because by co-operating with the police he would have implicated himself. But the guys' loyalty to an unwritten law transcended the fact that they had been at the point of committing a criminal offense, and so much so that they actually forgot this fact. And he knew that from this moment things would not be the same for them again. Something had happened to their relationship, particularly to his relationship with Ricky. More than ever he knew they could never be friends again, because somehow he represented an obstacle to the attainment of certain goals Ricky had imposed upon his life.

He stopped crying then, because it was not worth crying for people. He withdrew into his protective shell of cynicism, but he recognized it for what it was and could easily hide it from the world.

VI

"This is my brother's daughter from Cholula, don Juan," said Cirilo as Juan Rubio and his son Richard entered his house.

"Much pleasure in knowing you," said Juan Rubio, taking her hand. "Juan Rubio at your command."

"Equally," replied the young girl. "Pilar Ramírez, to serve you."

She turned to Richard, and they exchanged the introduction in the same manner. She was not shy, but appeared so because she was a woman from México. Not since he was a child and his family followed the crops had he seen a woman act like she acted. He was seeing his mother as she had been long ago. She spoke only if directly addressed, and he talked to her. She was from Cholula, in the state of México, she said, and her father was dead and so she was here. He said he had never known anyone from that far south, and she said she was sixteen years old. Once, she giggled as he spoke and he flushed, for he knew she was laughing at his Spanish, which was a CaliforniaMexican-American Castilian.

"I am a Pocho," he said, "and we speak like this because here in California we make Castilian words out of English words. But I can read and write in the Spanish, and I taught myself from the time I had but eight years."

"It matters not," she said. "I understand you perfectly well."

She was slight, yet breasty, with good legs, and very dark. And he thought her pretty, because to a Mexican swarthiness means beauty.

The others talked among themselves, so Richard and Pilar were allowed to enjoy their conversation until it was time to leave. He would come back, he thought, for she was interesting and pleasant, and he liked her. She could tell him about the México of today, not that of twenty years ago, which his parents knew.

He never saw her again, but his father did, and occasionally brought back word that she had asked for him, and, in fact, he kidded him about his "admirer." It did not occur to Richard that his father had his eye on her.

Then, one early morning, Richard came home from being with Zelda, to find his house ablaze with lights and his father in a rage. He had never seen him so angry. His face was livid, and when he spoke, saliva sprayed with his words and some trickled down the corner of his mouth.

"My daughters will not behave like whores!" he shouted.

"If I am a whore, it is having your blood that makes me one!" Luz stood up to him, shouting back.

"What hour is this—three o'clock in the morning—for a decent girl to be coming home?" he asked. "Where were you?"

"That is no concern of yours," she replied. "What I do is my business!"

The children were huddled against a wall, the smaller ones crying. Consuelo, in a soiled robe, also shrank back, she alone knowing what wrath could drive her husband to do.

"Tell me where you were!" he insisted. "This is still my house, and as long as you are in it, you answer to me!"

"Wake up!" screamed Luz, and her face was ugly. "This *your* house!" She laughed shrilly. "This is our house, and if we want, we can have you put out! Tell him, Mamá. He put the house in your name, in case something happened to him you would have no trouble! *Tell him, Mamá!*" she screamed. "Tell him something has happened to him!"

Juan Rubio hit her with the back of his hand, and she bounced off the wall but she did not fall. Again she screamed to Consuelo, and Consuelo, given courage by the utterance of that which she had lately been telling her daughters, lost her head and stepped forward, screeching, "Do not dare to touch her again, you brute!" She took hold of his arm, and he spun toward her, the force of his movement knocking her off balance, so she stumbled crazily through the door and landed on her face in the kitchen.

Richard stood on the opposite side, transfixed by the grotesque masque that was taking place before his eyes. A masque it surely was, for he did not know any of these people. In his mind, he was not sure any of it was real. Horrified and in anguish, he thought, *A bad dream! A real bad dream or a Goddamn dumb show!*

His sister brought him out of shock. "Stand there! Just stand there, you weak bastard, and watch this son of a bitch hit your mother!" She leaped at Juan Rubio's face with her hands, and very deliberately he hit her in the face with his fist. She did not get up.

Juan Rubio rushed out the door and down into the cellar. From his tool closet he took an axe, and began first on the wine barrels and then on the shelves upon shelves of preserves, and when he was done destroying everything he had built or accumulated with his own hands, he walked into the house, a specter drenched in wine, purple and ominous. "Out!" he shouted. "Out, everyone, for I am going to destroy this cancer!" But his family was incapable of moving, their fear was so great, and as he walked toward the cupboard, Richard tackled him from behind. Crying, tears streaming down his face, he pleaded, "No, Papá! No, Papá! It is worth nothing—all this!" And all the time he held on to the kicking legs of his father, and when he was shaken off and they were both on their feet, his father hit him a chopping blow with his great hand, and once more turned to what was now a duty. Richard came back again, dripping blood from his nose and mouth, and this time he jumped on his father's back, only to slip off, and as he fell his head struck the floor, knocking him unconscious.

Juan Rubio laid the axe almost gently on the table and picked up his son as easily as he would a child. He carried him into the bedroom and put him on the bed.

"Get water!" he said to his wife, who was tearing at her hair, screaming, "My son! My son!" But at that moment Richard opened his eyes.

He saw that the walls of the room were still standing and that his father and mother were there over him, strangely close together. His upper lip was numb, and he could feel a swelling along his nostrils. He tried to get up, but his father held him down.

"Get me a change of clothes," said Juan Rubio. "And make me a mochila of some of my things."

"Bueno, Juan," she said simply.

"You are leaving, then, my father?" asked Richard.

"Yes, but do not be disturbed. I will remain in the valley."

"It is time," said Richard, "and I am not disturbed. I am sad, true, but I am somehow happy."

Juan Rubio did not look at his son. Perhaps it was because of the many things that would remain unsaid between them. Finally, he looked into his son's eyes. "Yes," he said. "It is time, and I have waited overly long, but since I am able to do it after all, it was not wrong to wait. Do not cry, my son." He wiped a tear from Richard's face with the side of his thumb.

Richard took the hand that had always been at once so tender and so harsh. "I cannot keep myself from crying. Rare that always in this family I remember tears. When we are happy we cry, and when we have tragedy we cry."

Juan Rubio smiled. "That is because in the end we are Mexican. It is as simple as that," he said. "Once, I had an acquaintance"—and he laughed now as he spoke, so that his beautiful unbrushed teeth shone yellow—"who said that Mexicans were the most fortunate people in the world, because they ate strong chile and cried. When a Mexican has stomach trouble, this man said, it is usually a serious illness and he dies, but he will never have boils in the intestines or any of that sort of trouble. That is because we eat chile and are a lachrymose race."

"You did not like him, did you?"

"Why do you ask that?"

"Because you called him your acquaintance and 'this man.'"

"Well, he was not an intimate friend. We came to California together. He was a strange one; in fact I thought at times that he was one of 'those others.'"

"They have their place," said Richard.

Juan Rubio again looked into his son's eyes. "You have that much understanding, my son? . . . Then I think I can tell you that for a long time I thought you would become like that. Because you had the bad lot to live with a houseful of girls, and your mother protected you so much. I thought that if it happened so, I would try to understand it. And yet—I suppose because you are the only man in the family—I thought I would strangle you with my own hands, and to do that would mean that I would destroy myself, because although I have never told you, I feel about you as strongly as your mother does."

"I know."

Juan Rubio was not embarrassed. It seemed that he had all the time in the world to talk to his son, and what had happened a few minutes ago seemed forgotten. "This acquaintance I spoke about, he is a writer."

"That is what I will be," said Richard.

"Do you want that more than anything?"

"Yes, my father. More than anything, and forgive me if I put that before you and my mother."

"There is nothing to forgive," said Juan Rubio. "Only, never let anything stand in your way of it, be it women, money, or—what people talk about today—position. Only that, promise me—that you will be true unto yourself, unto what you honestly believe is right. And, if it does not stand in your way, do not ever forget that you are Mexican." It was Juan Rubio who was now crying.

"I could never forget that!" said Richard.

"One more thing," said his father. "I did not purposely strike your mother. I could not do that to you. Willingly I would tear this heart out with my hands when I hurt you in that way."

"I know."

"I go now," said Juan Rubio. "The sun will soon come out."

"You will be all right now, Papá?"

"I am all right *now*. I feel I am a man again."

"That is good," said Richard. Juan Rubio reached the door, and Richard said, "Papá."

He turned, and his son said, "¿Un abrazo?" They put their arms around each other in the Mexican way. Then Juan Rubio kissed his son on the mouth.

In the other room, Luz finally picked herself up off the floor and disappeared into her room.

On the bed, Richard heard the sound of the automobile fade away. Forgive me, my father, he thought. Forgive me because I cannot really talk with you, and for my transgressions against you. And I am sorry your life is very nearly spent. Soon, he knew, his father would be with another woman, for it was impossible that he should live without one. And he was happy for that, but, in spite of his intelligence, he was deeply hurt that he should have a woman other than his mother. He could never understand that part of himself—how he could feel in two distinct ways about something, with each feeling equally strong. This was one of the things he could not discuss with his father.

The tears were drying on his cheeks when he walked out of the room. His mother's face was flushed. He could see the regret and sorrow she would not admit even to herself. She moved about in a glow of victory, puttered here and there doing nothing whatsoever, but seemingly busy. Then she began to sweep the house, and the symbolism was so starkly real to him at that moment that he ran out the rear door, and, clutching at the trunk of the walnut tree, he uttered painful sobs until there were no tears left. After a bit, he went back into the kitchen and got a plateful of beans and some cold tortillas. He sat down to eat, and his mother said:

"I could have got that for you." She was suddenly full of solicitude, conscientious in her duty to the man of the house. Everything seemed to remind him. Things went badly for him, but he knew he must survive the next hour or he could never live with his mother again. The food was tasteless, even when smothered with chile. She tried to take his plate from in front of him. "Your food is cold. Let me warm it for you," she said.

"It is worth nothing, Mamá," he said. "Let it remain as it is." He could not tell her that it was impossible for him to have her do anything for him at this time.

She sat across from him and began to cry. "I cannot endure the knowledge that you are eating cold food," she said. "That is the reason I am here—your mother—to see that you are taken care of. Time enough when you are married to have to cook for yourself, and wash and iron for yourself and your wife, here in this country where all wives are lazies."

It was difficult to be cruel to her, particularly at this time, but he must do something that might stop the torture of continuing this conversation. In her ignorance, she was tearing him up inside. "Like my father had to do for himself, Mamá?" he asked.

"You are on his side," she sobbed. "If so, why did you not go with him?" With her it was still a matter of sides, and he tried to explain how he felt. And now he was pitying her.

"Mamá," he said, "there is no such thing in my mind. I have not gone with my father because you need me more—that is why. I love you both, but I do not love one of you more than the other, and if it fell upon his lot to need me, then I would go to him. You yourself, I know, would be unhappy if I forsook him. But what is between the two of you is not my affair. I am not provoked that he left. I am sorry that it had to be so, but I am not provoked, and I do not wish even to discuss whatever has happened between you. The only thing for me in the matter is that you are my mother and he is my father. Nothing else is changed. I am not changed, and I can never be changed by that which is outside of me. I can only be loyal to you both as well as I can."

She stopped crying. "You are right in many ways, my son. But he has deserted his wife and children. . . ."

"I will not discuss it, Mamá. Now or ever."

She did not mention his father again, but she began to talk of the new life they must make without him, and she sounded almost happy. Now that she was certain Richard would remain with her, she did not have the need to arouse his sympathy. He realized how frightened she had been. "You are the head of the family now, Richard. You are the man of the house," she said. "I know how much you wanted to go to the university, and I am filled with sadness that you will not be able to do so, for it is your duty to take care of us." It did not matter to him that she was sincere in her concern about that, and that she had somehow completely absolved herself of any taint of guilt for what had happened. But he could not allow her to believe that he was doing this for any reason other than the fact that he desired to do it.

"It is not a duty, Mamá," he said. "I am doing what I am doing because I do not want to do anything else at the moment, but please do not mistake my motives. It would only make you hurt much later. I told you it is not my life which has been changed, but yours and my father's. I do not belong here any more. I do not even belong in this town any more, and when the time comes that I want to go to school, Mamá, I will do so. I will remain until I must leave, and that is all."

She smiled, and through her smile he knew that she did not believe him. She was so full of plans now that she was like a child, so he reached across and kissed her cheek. "We should all go together to the church, little son," she said. "We are now starting on a new life, and it would be a good thing to receive a blessing from the Lord." It was suddenly too much once more, and now he must really hurt her.

"You received one blessing already when you were married, full of sacredness and solemnity. It did not help. No, Mamá. You go to your church and light the candles to your God. I am finished with such things."

Her face was white, and for a moment he thought that she would fall from her chair. "What are you saying? What blasphemy is this?"

He said, "Please, Mamá. I do not wish to make you unhappy, but you are forcing me to do so. I have left the Church. It is now a long time that I have not been to Mass, although I have believed all along. But now I find that I am through believing. I have not told you of this, because of what it would do to you—of what it is doing to you."

"You do not believe! What is this you do not believe? You do not believe what?"

"I no longer believe in God," he said, and was surprised at himself that he had dared finally to say the thing aloud. The maybe-maybe-what-if-I'm-wrong? thoughts did not come to his mind, and the apprehension and dizzy feeling that he always experienced at such thoughts did not come, and at last he was really free.

She cried then, long, painful sobs, and he did nothing to comfort her, for he was out of it completely. When she calmed down a bit, she questioned, striving to find an explanation for this tragedy. She was not angry—she could not even feel sorry for him yet, her torment was so great.

His life! How could he possibly live the good life? Without Christian principles, his children would suffer, and, worse, he could never teach them goodness without the help of the true faith. She found many such arguments to negate the words he had just spoken, but in the end it was simply "Why? WHY?"

In spite of himself, he could not remain indifferent to her. He went to his knees beside her and held her close. "It is a very difficult thing, my mother, to make you understand. It was most difficult for me to arrive at my final conclusion about religion. Now it is impossible for me to continue living a lie. I am good, though. Even in the way that you mean 'good' I am good, and in my way I am a better Christian than most Christians I know. And if my behavior can be called Christian, it is because I agree with most of the Decalogue and not because it is a Christian thing to do so. I do not like some of the things they do, these Christians. I do not have to fear God in order to love man. That is one of my weaknesses, perhaps—that I love man too much. Nor do I need God in my hour of strongest need.

"But you, Mamá, you must believe, because for you it is

not a lie—because you could not live without your God. Without Him, you would be dead before you really die."

She accepted her defeat, and it was clear to him that as long as she could keep him by her side, nothing else mattered. Her love for him was so strong that even his renunciation of the eternal life was not too great for her to suffer. It was not too healthy, this thing, she knew. Yet it was bearable, because she realized that she had but a small part of him. She had lost her men—both of them. And already there was a look of mourning on her face— An emblem more convincing than if she had donned black garments.

Outside, light grayness replaced the dark, and Richard was happy the night was over, for, indeed, bad things happened at night.

from *Chicano*

Richard Vasquez

David Stiver and Mariana Sandoval found all parking places taken for a block on each side of the house where the party was to take place. It was a warm evening and as they walked back toward the house, Stiver examined the neighborhood. He tried to analyze how his feelings had changed about the community since he had become somewhat familiar with it.

"How do you feel about East Los Angeles now?" she asked, guessing his thoughts. He reflected a moment.

"You're trying to teach me to be honest," he said, "so I'll try to tell you. One thing, I feel as though you're protecting me. Just being with me. You're kind of my passport."

"Do you feel uncomfortable still?"

". . . Yes, I certainly don't feel like I belong here."

She walked in silence for a moment. "I think everybody belongs anywhere. Or at least they should. But of course that's not the way it is."

They pased a house with several persons sitting on the front porch. One man strummed a guitar, while the other sang.

"Would I be safe, really, walking down this street alone?"

"You'd be safe from all those people. It's the young punks, the rowdies, who might give you a bad time. You'd be pretty safe in a neighborhood like this with just homes."

David looked at the homes. All seemed at least thirty years old. Many had small lawns in front, some had old jalopies in the front yard.

"Look at that place. Five cars, all heaps of junk, in the front yard and in the driveway. Why do they keep them there?"

She laughed. "That's called 'chicano landscaping.' I don't know why there's so many here. There's some joke, I don't know how it goes, about a guy who got so drunk he couldn't find his way back to Boyle Heights, but he knew he was getting closer by the number of junked cars on the front lawns.

You're the sociologist. Why do you think there's so many heaps around? Nobody really needs them. If a car's worth a hundred dollars, and it cost a hundred and fifty to get it fixed, an American will throw it away. A chicano will give you ten dollars for it."

"That reminds me of a Greek or maybe it was an Egyptian fable. A man loved diamonds terribly, so somehow he got a magician to turn all pebbles and stones into diamonds. Of course they immediately lost all value, but he still thought they were as beautiful as ever. The funny part was, certain people, even though diamonds were worthless, couldn't help collecting them and hoarding them. They were still obsessed with diamonds. The pattern was too strong to break."

They came to the house. The party was well under way. They stopped in front, to finish their talk in private on the sidewalk.

"And you think somehow that's similar to all these cars?" she asked with interest.

"Yes. I think until so recently a car, any car, was a luxury item to some classes that just the ownership, even if it's a financial liability, is really an obsession for status."

She looked at him admiringly, and he realized he always inwardly warmed when she did. "I think you're right about that, David."

"You see," he explained, "a car is something more than just a mechanical possession. It must be registered in your name, you must get the pink slip, and most important of all, to some, the great big state must make a record of little ol' *you* as the owner and no one else can claim it without your written consent in the form of your signature. When it comes to owning a car, the richest man with the biggest Cadillac is registered in the same way, by the same government agency, must submit the same material and papers and receives the identical ownership certificate as the poorest dishwasher with his jalopy. He pays more for his license, the rich man, but this is really equal treatment. Real equality."

"I see," she agreed. "You're saying it isn't the value of a car that's so important, it's owning it."

"Yes. The mechanics of ownership. I think all this registration, sending to Sacramento, your address, all this, is really as satisfying to your people, if not more so, than calling a pile of junk your own. By the way, just what kind of a thing is this we're going to here?" He indicated the house.

She pulled his arm, starting toward the front door. "Come on," she said.

The main body of persons was in the back yard. David estimated sixty or seventy people seated, standing, or wandering around. In one corner there was lively music. It seemed everybody was singing, laughing, shouting or drinking. Mariana tugged his arm and he bent to hear her.

"This isn't what us kids would call a young folks' party. No swingers here. The few younger ones our age you see here are either square or going along with it for the old folks. There's Mom and Dad over there. See?"

Stiver looked and saw a group of a dozen or so standing around a small goat. The animal was about half grown, and looked alarmed and confused by the noise and activity.

"What's the goat for?" David asked.

"To eat," she said.

"But he's *alive*," David said uneasily.

"Yes, right now, anyway."

Stiver watched. Pete was feeling the goat's head, talking, arguing loudly, a little drunkenly, with another man, in Spanish. The other man said something, and the group roared with laughter, except Pete. He shook his head and argued some more, gesturing emphatically. The other man shook his head in disagreement. The two were fairly shouting at each other.

"What are they saying?" Stiver asked.

Mariana laughed, squeezing his arm. "My father is saying that the color of the goat's little horns indicates the meat will be very tough. He says a purple color means it hasn't eaten the right vitamins. The other man says no, the goat has eaten mainly leftover beans and watermelon rinds, and that makes the most tender, delicious meat of all."

"Does your dad really know about goats?"

She chuckled, turning away. "No. He doesn't know a thing about them. I really think he's making that up, about purple horns."

"Then why the argument?"

"Because. Dad's barely over five feet tall. He's funny looking. He's successful, and he knows he can make people laugh all night with his ridiculous statements. He's aware everybody knows he's lying. Didn't you have psychology in college?"

David smiled. "You mean he's a ham."

She looked at him with affectionate appreciation. "That's exactly what I mean. Come on. Let's see the mariachis."

"Mariachis. Those are musicians. Right?"

"Right."

As they made their way across the wide concrete slab which took up half the entire back yard, Stiver looked for traces of Spanish or Mexican dress or décor. Subconsciously, he realized, he'd pictured piñatas, gay yellow and red pinks and bullfight posters. A string of bare bulbs lighted the area. A dilapidated garage was at one side, its doors open to show a jalopy standing on concrete blocks, the wheels long since borrowed for another vehicle. He noticed that in general the older folks wore old sweaters, shawls and baggy dresses or trousers, while the middle-aged generation wore outmoded suits with no necktie, and the younger ones near his age dressed fairly nicely, with an inevitable anachronism such as highly pointed shoes or string ties.

A girl with yellow hair and freckles stood out among the crowd. She and Mariana saw each other at the same time. The girl was with a dark youth in tight trousers and suede jacket. As the couples came together the yellow-haired girl was looking at David.

"Betty!" Mariana said, genuine pleasure showing. "Hello, Rudy. Betty, you've never met Dave. Dave, this is Betty."

Stiver nodded to her and shook hands with Rudy. He smiled. "So you're the one," he said lightly to Elizabeth.

"She's my white liberal friend I was telling you about," Mariana laughed.

Elizabeth smiled plainly. "And it's not always easy," she said. Stiver noticed she was appraising him from head to toe.

David tried not to react as he saw Rudy crudely and obviously jerk his head, indicating he wanted to talk with Mariana alone. He saw a look of helpless annoyance cross Elizabeth's face, and saw quick anger in Mariana as she glanced at him. David nodded and Mariana stepped away a few paces with Rudy. Elizabeth stood close to David, talking quietly.

"You get used to it after a while. At first it seems these people have no manners or consideration. But actually it's just a way of thinking. Or not thinking."

Stiver looked at her. "Maybe he has something important to say to her."

"Even if it was important, which it's not, it's the sort of

thing you never get used to around here. It's very typical, this business of having something secret to discuss. Interrupting others to go off and whisper. It seems from deeprooted feelings of inferiority."

"You sound like a psych major."

"I am. Cal State, L.A."

"You've lived in this part of town all your life?"

"Just about. Mariana and I grew up together."

"I'd give anything if I could say her name the way you do."

"It's a beautiful name, isn't it? When it's said right. But I hate to hear 'Merry-anna.' Makes me want to puke."

Stiver laughed. "I'll do my best to say it right. The broad 'A' isn't so hard, it's the 'R.' "

They were both watching Mariana as she talked with Rudy.

Elizabeth said, "She's something awfully special to us, that girl. We've been best friends since about the third grade, but she's more than that. She's sort of my special project."

Stiver was puzzled. "How's that?"

"My dad is one of the world-changers. We moved down here because he thought we could do some good for the cause. Everybody in East L.A. falls into the culturally deprived category. We've tried like hell to give Mariana some realistic values. I couldn't talk her into going on to school after we graduated from high school. But I did talk her into the business school she attends. After seeing her develop into such an utterly sweet, unpretentious, proud girl—her looks haven't spoiled her—it would have killed us to see her marry some factory worker at eighteen and start having babies every year. A girl like Mariana belongs to the world. If someone could only get her out of East L.A."

Stiver was still watching Mariana. "Wonder what they're talking about," he mused.

"Rudy's pestering her for a date."

Stiver showed surprise.

"That's right," she went on. "He's with me, she's with you, but that doesn't stop him from calling her aside and pestering her. Stick around. You'll get used to it."

David saw Mariana shake her head, turning away from Rudy. She raised her voice so the others could hear. "I said *no!* Please leave me alone." Rudy's face darkened with embarrassment as he realized the others heard. Then he wheeled and walked quickly away.

Mariana joined David and Elizabeth. "I'm sorry I had to

do that. Say it out loud, to embarrass him. But these things have to be dealt with."

"So he just leaves Betty standing here," Stiver mused.

"Don't worry," Elizabeth said. "He'll be back. He's lost face, but he'll get over it."

A man at a table nearby was serving punch in little paper cups. Mariana addressed him: "Pablo!"

The man turned his attention to her, frank admiration on his face.

"Mande?"

"Give us two, please," she said. He handed her two cups.

Stiver took one. "I'm learning a little," he said, "but what was that he said to you? Sounded like 'mande.' "

"Yes, 'mande,' " Mariana nodded. "It means, let's see, actually it means 'command me.' Kind of gallant, isn't it?"

Stiver mulled it over a little. They drank their punch and talked with Elizabeth a while. Although not interested in her personally, David made a mental note to sometime talk to Elizabeth more about these people. He had a lot of questions to ask, and the more he was around Mariana, the more questions he wanted answered.

In a few minutes Mariana said, "David?"

He snapped erect and looked into her face. "Command me," he said.

She laughed. "Let's go see the musicians."

The music became louder as they walked toward a group of perhaps thirty people surrounding a dozen musicians.

David looked at her, puzzled. "How come the trumpets?"

She stopped, pulling him to a halt as she did so. "This is Mexican music. Not what you call Spanish. You think of Spanish music as soft guitars, fancy rhythms, castanets. I know. But listen to this." She pulled him through the crowd, up to the musicians.

There were a pair of guitars, three violins, two huge bass guitars, three singers, and two trumpeters. As David watched, he heard the trumpets playing a soft accompaniment. Then as the verse ended, for a few brief measures the trumpets went into a wild loud duet, zigzagging, triple-tonguing and flutter-tonguing. Then, as the next verse started and the singers began again, the trumpets returned to the soft accompaniment. By the time this was repeated two or three times, David began to like it. He noticed most attention was given to the trumpeters during those brief two or three measure fillers, during which they displayed their maximum talent, volume and dexerity. Evidently, there were innumerable stanzas to this particular song, and about the fourth time through, two men from the crowd stepped forth and almost by force took the trumpets away and took over the soft accompaniment. However, at the end of the verse, these two outdid the former trumpet players for the two brief measures, and applause broke out among the spectators as the singers began the next verse. Near the end, a near drunk man grabbed the trumpet from one player and delivered dazzling ornaments and embellishments when the singers finished and were catching their breaths for the next stanza. David saw it was a show-off contest, and evidently everybody knew how to "fill in."

"Come, I'll show you something else," Mariana said, pulling him toward the crowd around the goat. For the first time, David noticed a large hole in the ground with a glowing bed of coals and hot stones nearby. He watched as one man held the goat's rear feet and another held its forelegs, while yet another held the frightened animal's head.

"Jorobado! Jorobado," they called. "Where's that damn Jorobado!"

Pete was standing close. All looked around for Jorobado. "That damn guy," Pete said in English to no one. "He wanted to do the honors and now he's gone. I . . ."

"Here he comes now," a man holding the goat said. "Jorobado! Andale! I can't hold this damn thing like this all night."

David recoiled inwardly as he looked at the man called Jorobado. His face was cruelly twisted out of shape and he had a huge hump on his spine, causing him to half drag his feet as he walked, waddling almost like a duck. Jorobado came forward, pulling from his belt a shiny hunting knife.

"Here I am, guys," he said, speaking English with a fairly thick accent. "All you lilies! Where would you be if it wasn't for your good bloodthirsty friend Jorobado?"

A woman seated nearby jumped to her feet. "Bloodthirsty! I'm glad you said that, Jorobado. Wait. Wait. I won't be a momento." She ran into the house. Jorobado stood looking down at the little goat. "She has all night, and then she forgets," he said, trying to look swaggeringly like a pirate, David thought. In a few seconds the woman returned from the house with a metal basin.

"Okay," she said, holding the basin under the goat's throat.

Although it was happening fast, David was aware he was about to see something he didn't particularly care to see. But he was fascinated. He glanced around to observe the general reaction. He saw some of the women averting their eyes, others walking away, smiling squeamishly in mild disgust. He looked at Mariana, and found her watching him, her face serious. He returned his attention to the goat. The animal was still being held. Jorobado placed the blade of the knife against the goat's neck and in one quick jerk, cut the neck half through. The creature jerked wildly as it tried to jump, but couldn't move its feet. Its lungs still breathed, and little jets of bloody foam shot out of each side of the neck. Its eyes rolled upward, and the basin nearby filled as the heart sent its life blood gushing through the severed jugular veins. Then the goat collapsed.

A huge fat man wearing a white apron appeared, carrying a large butcher knife. "Help me. Don't make me do all the work," he said to the others. The carcass was laid on a canvas, and the butchering began. David watched as the belly was slit expertly, and the entrails removed. "Para los perros," someone said. David understood it meant "for the dogs." The man in the apron was obviously a professional butcher, David realized, as he saw him skin the goat, cut off the hoofs and tail. David was a little puzzled as he saw them leave the head attached and placed the whole body in a large tub. A heavy burlap cloth was placed over the goat, and then the tub was lowered into the bed of glowing coals and hot stones. Then several men took shovels and covered coals, stones and goat with a foot or more of dirt. The fat man in the white apron wiped his bloody hands and said, "Now let's have that party!"

The crowd in the back yard had grown, and groups were collecting here and there to talk in loud voices. Bottles of wine were on tables everywhere, and all present seemed to be drinking heavily. Mariana and David walked slowly around the groups.

"That man, Horo . . . what's he called? The one who killed the goat."

"Jorobado?" she said.

"Yes, he sort of gave me a chill. He's so . . . deformed."

"That's why he's called Jorobado." David looked puzzled. She went on: "There's a famous French book. Haven't you read it? *El Jorobado de Notre Dame*. It's a classic."

David thought. "De Notre Dame. Of Notre Dame. Oh,

the Hunchback . . . you mean, that's what you call him? Hunchback?"

She looked at him with sincerity. "I'm beginning to see how hard it is for you to understand, David. I only hope you'll . . ."

"No," he said. "I'm beginning to see a little, myself."

They came to an old woman seated on a bench. She had a shawl over her head and wore a dress that came to her ankles. She smiled at Mariana, showing toothless gums, and said something in Spanish. David heard Mariana say a sentence with "gracias" in it. Then she turned to him.

"She says you're a very handsome gringo, and she says you also look like you're very rich."

"What'd you tell her?"

"I told her thanks, and she's right, you're rich, handsome and 'muy simpatico.' A nice person."

The old woman grinned broadly, trying in vain to conceal her toothlessness with her hand. She took a drink of what looked like red wine in a glass and said something else to Mariana. Mariana conversed briefly with her and then translated.

"She asked if we two are in love."

David smiled. "What'd you tell her?"

"I told her I love you, but that's all I know."

Stiver looked sharply at Mariana. She returned his gaze serenely. The old woman spoke again, grinning broadly.

"She wants to know if you'll have a drink with her."

David saw there was a glass with a dark red fluid in it on the table in front of the old woman. "Tell her yes . . . "

"It's blood," Mariana cut in. David had started to reach for the empty glass the old woman held out, but he froze. He looked at Mariana, feeling his stomach muscles contract involuntarily. He started to stammer. Mariana said nothing, did nothing. There was a little smile on her face.

"Tell her . . . I . . ." To his great relief, the old woman burst into laughter, and David was able to graciously refuse. Mariana tugged him and they walked on.

"How come," he asked, "nobody introduces anybody else to anyone?"

"That's just one of the stupid ways of the chicanos," she answered philosophically. "This party isn't so bad, because almost everyone knows each other. But usually, half the people don't know anybody, and unlike the gringos, nobody has the courage or whatever it is to walk up and introduce himself, so everyone just stands around, hoping conversation will develop somehow."

"Tell me," he said as they strolled, "is this . . . drinking of blood, is it pretty common?"

She laughed a little. "No," she said emphatically, "it's not. Just the old-timers do it. And I think they do it mostly to get a reaction. I guess years ago it was the ordinary thing, when everybody slaughtered their own cattle. They still make sausages out of blood." She looked at him. "You can buy blood sausages in lots of Anglo stores, can't you?"

He thought a moment. "Yes, I guess so. I guess that's not much different from drinking it."

She snorted. "Oh yes it is, David. It's lots different, and you know it. But I'll bet you like your steak rare. With blood running out."

He smiled reflectively. "Yes, I do."

"And I'll bet if no one's looking you sop up the blood with your bread."

"No, I mash my potato into it and get it that way."

They both laughed.

Two hours later about a third of the guests were in various stages of collapse or near collapse. David had refused most of the dozens of bottles or glasses of wine offered him and Mariana had sipped sparingly. David saw Pete walk unsteadily over to the side of the yard and begin vomiting. He nudged Mariana and directed her attention to him. Another man hurried over to Pete and steered him to the nearby fence. He pushed Pete's head over the fence. "If you have to throw up, don't do it in my yard," he said.

"I take it he's our host," David said quietly to Mariana. She nodded. Pete retched over the fence again and again.

"What about the neighbor that lives there?" David asked. "Maybe he doesn't want vomit in his yard either."

Mariana pointed to a man vomiting on the other side of the property. "You're right. That's him throwing up in the yard on the other side."

David saw the humor in the situation. "Why do they all drink so much they get sick?"

"Some of them want to. To make room for that. Look there."

David saw some men had uncovered the roasting goat and with pot holders were lifting out the huge tub. They carried it to one of the tables and lifted the carcass out onto a large wooden board. Many of the guests were beyond the hunger stage, but two dozen or so crowded around the table, sniffing and exclaiming. The man with the white apron stood by the goat, butcher knife in hand. Plates were passed around.

"Wait! Wait!" the man said, looking around. "Where's our gringo guest?" His eyes fell on David. "Come forward, please sir," he said to David. David hesitated, unsure, and Mariana pulled him along to the table.

"For you," the man said to David. "The special treat."

He took the knife and expertly cut one eyeball of the goat and placed it on a plate. He held it out to David, and everyone stood watching. David regarded the steaming eyeball, not knowing just what to do. The eyeball stared up blankly at him. David took the plate and looked miserably around. All the faces were serious. Someone put a fork in his hand and he stared stupidly at the fork. He looked pleadingly at Mariana. *Save me, please,* he seemed to say. But she only smiled a little. David again looked at the two dozen dark faces watching him earnestly. Then he raised the fork and tried to cut the eye, which was nearly the size of a golf ball. He found it very tough and leathery. He pressed harder. Suddenly the huge man in the white apron threw back his head and rocked with laughter, clapping David so hard on the back he almost dropped the plate. Then the others began laughing. It was a joke, he saw. They hadn't really expected him to go through with it. The big man stopped laughing and took the plate from David's hand.

"Look," he said, popping the still steaming eyeball into his mouth. He chewed vigorously. "Eyes are good for the sight. You notice I don't wear glasses? That's because I eat eyes. It's the best thing in the world for the sight." David laughed.

Someone shouted, "You're eating the wrong part. You should be eating the brains." This brought a swell of mirth. A woman who David guessed was the man's wife pushed her way through to him.

"I think you must eat too much tongue. Always you talk."

The big man grinned. "Honey, tell 'em what other part I eat. When it's a male goat like this." The woman blushed and looked away. "Go on. Tell 'em how I am. And past fifty years, too."

"That goat meat was out of this world," David said to Mariana as they finished the meal. "If you could sell this at a restaurant you could . . ." He was interrupted by a crowd talking loudly. Looking, they saw Jorobado, the hunchback, pushing some other men out of his way.

"I know when I'm sober enough to drive," Jorobado was saying, struggling toward his car parked in the drive beside the house.

"Don't do it. You'll wreck," someone warned him.

"I only live two blocks," he said with determination, "I'm going home, and nobody better not stop me."

He was barely able to walk, but he staggered to his car. The others watched as he got in and started the engine. The tires squealed as he backed up suddenly. David could hear the engine roar. Then there was another screech of tires and a thud. David and Mariana joined the others hurrying to the front to see what had happened.

Jorobado had missed the driveway entrance by ten feet, and the rear wheels were suspended above the gutter, spinning uselessly, as the weight of the car rested on the frame, atop the curb. Jorobado raced the engine, but the wheels just spun in the air. Finally he got out, looking resentfully at the others gathering around.

"Now look what the hell you did," Jorobado accused. "I'm stuck." He surveyed the situation, started to fall over, and leaned against the car. He staggered to the front bumper and pushed it in vain. Then he turned to the others.

"Help me, god dammit! We can push this son-of-a-bitch into the street if we try."

The big butcher came forward. "I told you not to drive. You're too drunk to walk, even."

"Just shut up and help me push," Jorobado persisted, still pushing by himself. "If you don't wanna help me, then get the hell away. You god-damn meat cutter."

Although there were perhaps thirty people gathered around Jorobado's car, no one offered to help free it. David first noticed the police car driving slowly toward them. It pulled up directly in front of the other car. David saw one officer inside pick up the radio mike and speak briefly, then replace the mike. The group had grown quiet. Jorobado leaned against his car for support, looking at the prowl car. The two officers got out and approached them. They walked to Jorobado, who was standing beside the driver's seat. A bright street light illuminated the entire scene. The officers were Anglos.

"Having a little trouble here?" one asked.

"He stuck his car," someone said from the group. David felt Mariana's hand grip his arm.

"This your car?" the officer asked Jorobado, looking him over.

"Yeah, it's mine," Jorobado said.

Both officers walked to the rear wheels and examined the situation. David noticed they glanced up and down the street, expectantly. Then they walked back to Jorobado, "Were you driving it when this happened?" one asked.

"Yeah, I only live two blocks . . ."

"How much you had to drink?" the other officer asked. David saw they were young, middle twenties perhaps.

"I'm not drunk, if that's what you mean," Jorobado said.

The officers surveyed the crowd, looking casual and confident. Then one said, "You better step over to the police car, fella," to Jorobado. The hunchback shuffled, staggered toward the patrol car parked in the center of the street. Its red light on top was blinking. The crowd surged forward as far as the curb to watch.

"Leave him alone," the white-aproned man hollered. "We'll take him home. He only lives two blocks."

One of the officers turned, pointing his night stick at the crowd. "You people better stay out of this," he warned. The other officer reached into his pocket and produced a coin. He placed it on the pavement in front of Jorobado. "Now. Let's see you pick it up," he ordered.

"He can't. Can you see he's crippled?" a voice from the crowd said. The officer paid no attention.

"Come on, Pancho. Pick it up," the officer commanded Jorobado, misshapen as he was, had to brace himself against the patrol car to bend over. His grip on the car slipped and he started to fall. The officer caught him and whirled him around, taking out his handcuffs at the same time. He wrestled with Jorobado trying to force his hands behind him. Jorobado cried out.

"Don't! I can't put my hands behind my back. They don't bend that way because of my hunchback!" The officer continued to wrestle him into position. The other officer turned his attention to the crowd.

"Stand back, all of you," he said, a hand resting on his pistol. He glanced down the street. David followed his glance and saw another flashing red light coming. Within seconds the two patrol cars braked to a halt and two officers climbed out of each car, hurrying toward the scene of the struggle. Two turned their attention to the crowd while the other two grabbed Jorobado by the arms and bent them behind him. Jorobado yelled: "My arms! Stop it!" And then the handcuffs were on him.

Jorobado was kicking at his captors, swearing loudly. The three officers picked him up bodily and threw him into the rear seat of the patrol car. The crowd, led by the meat cutter, moved off the curb into the street. All the policemen turned to face them, their faces looking grave, ready to do battle in the line of duty.

"Now, all of you get back up on the curb!" one officer shouted. The crowd edged forward. "Leave him alone." "He's a cripple." "Untie his hands, it hurts him." "He's not drunk, he's lame." David, apparently none of the others, noticed another police car arrive, and in a few seconds another, and then another. David looked the other way and saw more. A dozen squad cars were either there or arriving. Policemen leaped out with shotguns. The butcher, leading the others, started toward the two original arresting officers.

"Look, mister, that's no way to treat a guy when . . . "

A policeman ran to intercept him and the two collided. The officer went down, turning a somersault backward. As though it were a signal, another officer leaped forward, shouting, "Assaulting an officer. You're under arrest!" As the meat cutter turned to face him he was struck down by a night stick. He went to his knees, blood coming from his nose. Two policemen were on him instantly, bending his arms behind his back and in a second or two he was also handcuffed. The crowd surged forward, voices rising hysterically, and as though by magic, a solid line of fifteen policemen formed abreast, each leveling a shotgun on the group. "Raul!" a policemen with sergeant's stripes hollered. A Mexican-American officer came forward. He didn't need to be told what to do. He stood between the row of shotguns and the crowd.

It was the first time in his life David had ever faced a loaded shotgun. The many headlights of the patrol cars made the scene bright as day, and he could see each gun clearly, looking hard, cold and hideous.

"Go on home, all of you!" The Mexican-American officer ordered.

"Since when do you order us off the street?" came a voice.

Raul stood defiantly, glaring at them. "You can't do any

good. The law has been broken, and it must be enforced. Somebody will get hurt if you come any closer."

David saw fear on Raul's face. A trapped fear, as though he had no side to go to. The crowd pressed closer, angry voices rose. Less than ten feet separated the line of policemen with shotguns and the group from the party. David noticed, though the others apparently did not, that the meat cutter had been placed in a car and whisked off. Now the car with Jorobado in the back seat started moving away slowly.

David looked at Mariana. Her face was white. "My God!" he said. "This is unbelievable!" As he looked at her he saw her face contort with terror. Looking back on the street he saw Pete forcing his way to the front of the group confronting Officer Raul, who stood his ground; the buffer between Anglo police and his people. Pete began talking rapidly, but relatively quietly, in Spanish. The two cars with the prisoners had left the scene. David found his heart pounding. "What's he saying? Good God! Somebody's going to get killed."

Pete talked at length, shouting Raul down when the officer tried to speak. The police sergeant gave a signal and the shotgun line began falling back. "Okay, let's get out of here," the sergeant said. The officers began getting in their cars, leaving Raul and one patrol car with a frightened Anglo policeman waiting for him. Pete kept up his monologue, and Raul said nothing, looking indifferent. Then Raul turned his back and walked toward the remaining squad car. As he did so the crowd broke into angry curses, shouting threateningly. Raul climbed in and as he slammed the door the tires squealed and the street was empty except for the party-makers and the parked cars.

The group remained in the street, talking angrily, apparently having no plan to disperse. Mariana pulled David by the arm and they started walking down the sidewalk.

"What's going to happen? To those two they took?"

"They'll go to jail. Be tried for resisting arrest, being drunk, and maybe a half dozen other things."

"But the man, the butcher. He did nothing. That officer bumped him deliberately and then pretended to fall down."

Mariana smiled bitterly at him. "You want to really be the white liberal? Then go to the court trial and tell that to the judge. It won't do any good, but you'll be getting a real lesson in sociology."

"I still can't believe it happened. They . . . they were ready to start *shooting*."

"You're very right. You think everybody there didn't realize that? And in every bunch of Anglo cops, there's one who's itching to pull the trigger. You never know which one, but there's one there."

"If I hadn't seen that, I wouldn't believe it. Does this happen often? The shotguns and phony arrests, I mean?"

"Only in East Los Angeles. No, I take that back. It happens in Watts too. Maybe worse there."

"Your dad. What was he saying to that chicano cop?" He used the word without being aware of it at first.

She laughed. "David, you wouldn't believe what Dad was saying. He called him everything from the son of a two-peso whore to the father of perverted children, with lots more in between. Then he called him a Leo Carrillo."

"A Leo Carrillo? He was an actor."

"Yes, he was an actor. An actor who acted just like the white man told him to act, who acted out the white man's image of a Mexican exactly like the white man wanted to think about Mexicans. In Watts they call a guy like Leo Carrillo an Uncle Tom."

They were walking toward his car, and he stopped her and placed his hands on her shoulders. "Mariana—do I say it right yet? Your name?"

She smiled. "Pretty close. The single R is almost trilled."

"Mariana, I'm going to do something about this. What I saw tonight." She was silent, serious. "Don't you believe me?"

"I believe you may try. Dad tried to help some poor Negroes once. A contractor was cheating them. They started calling him 'Nigger-lover,' and he wound up getting fired."

"Mark my words, Mariana, I'll see that someone in a high position hears about what happened here tonight. If I have to I'll go to the president of the university to get pressure put on to bring all this to light."

She shook her head. "David, how can you tell them what East L.A. is like, when you don't even know yourself? Let's . . . let's go to your apartment. I know it's late, but I want to tell you lots of things you never dreamed of."

It was after two in the morning as they sat together on the couch in Stiver's apartment, Mariana talking on and on, for the first time in her life, he realized, expressing how she felt about the injustices she'd seen in the communities where she was raised. He watched her face as she talked softly, her voice becoming softer when she was angry, sometimes her eyes narrowing as she recalled frustration.

" . . . and then, Dad was nervous as he argued with the policeman, and he took out a package of cigarettes and opened them. You know how there's a little bit of cellophane paper that comes off the top? Well, he dropped it and it blew into the street. The policeman became furious. 'You trying to needle me?' he asked. 'You can get a $500 fine for throwing trash on the street. Now go pick it up. Pronto.' A little crowd had gathered, and the policeman stopped traffic while Dad got out on the street and found the little bit of cellophane. He made Dad put it in the car ashtray, and said Dad should be glad he wasn't writing him up on the anti-litter law instead of just an illegal turn. I've never forgotten that, even though I was little, nor how Dad just wouldn't talk the rest of the day. But instead of driving to the beach, where we were headed, he turned around and we went to see Grandma and Grandpa in Irwindale. Whenever Dad gets real upset and hurt, he always wants to go there."

He took her chin in his hand and tilted her head up.

"Tomorrow I'm going to do something about what happened at the party tonight."

"What are you going to do?"

He paused before answering. "I'm going to take a complaint to the proper place, wherever that is. I'm going to tell someone, the chief of police, if I have to, what happened. I'm sure it's not generally known the police pull shotguns and provoke arrests. I'm going to bring it to light."

She smiled genuinely. "You're turning into a knight in shining armor, David." She sipped her coffee. "I believed you would all along. I think I worked at making you fall in love with me."

He blinked. Uneasily: "I wasn't aware I'd mentioned it."

She looked at him wide-eyed. "I guess that shows how positive I am of impressions I get from people. You do love me, don't you?"

He looked away, a little exasperated. "You've tried to teach me to be honest. It's hard. Yes, I do, Mariana. So much, I never would have believed it. At first it was . . . "

"At first it was just me. The way I looked. I know I look good to men." She smiled. "How I know! First I was different, exotic to you. But I knew this would happen. It's not just me you love now. It's something more. Something very important."

He took both her hands, pulling her closer, looking into her eyes to see what it was that made him feel the way he did. With a start he realized she was a mature woman, ready to be a mother—more so than any girl he'd ever known, and yet she was softness and sex. It was this combination he found maddeningly desirable. He wondered idly if he suffered a little from Oedipus complex or if he had a little of that rare maturity that looked upon sex and pregnancy and parenthood as all part of the same emotional frame of reference.

"I want you, Mariana," he said simply.

She rose. "I know. I think it's the proper time."

He looked puzzled, then, "Oh, you mean, the right time of the . . ."

"No," a trace of a smile, "I mean it's all right for us. We're ready."

She walked surely into the bedroom. He felt hammers at his temples as he went in. She stood, by the tall dresser and bed. She only gave him a glance, and then took off her sweater. A little smile as she unbuttoned her blouse. He watched, sharpened to the marrow by the sight of her bare shoulders. He found himself holding his breath as she pulled back the covers of the bed, clad only in bra and half-slip, and leaned back against the bedstead waiting. She seemed incredibly calm. He sat on the bed and she ran her fingers through his hair.

Her voice sounded tiny and he could barely hear her say, "Come on." He fidgeted with his tie, then threw it down. He fumbled at his collar button. He gave it a yank and the button popped off and landed on her bare midriff. He was aware he was surprised to see that her midsection and shoulders were even-colored, surprised that she was not white underneath her clothes like all the others were so bleach-white. He reached for the button, smiling a little foolishly, but she was quicker and snatched the button away. As she pressed against his back with her hands, her fist with the button was clenched tightly.

It was two days a dozen or so phone calls later when David Stiver pulled his car into a lot near the Civic Center and walked to the police building. As he passed a bronze sculpting of three figures near the entrace he recalled dully the work had been the subject of a theme paper by an art major he knew. He knew he was not one of those people who could look at something arty and tell if it was good or not, and he dismissed it. Entering, he was directed to the office of the man with whom he had an appointment.

The office was paneled, quiet and plush for a police department, he thought as he waited. Presently the man came in. David wondered if he would have automatically disliked him before this whole business . . .

The man looked at David as though his name had just slipped his mind a moment before.

"You're . . . "

"David Stiver."

"Oh yes. I talked with you on the phone. And also your professor . . . "

"Right." David tried to fit him to a type and decided he could have been the youngest coach of the Big Ten Conference. He was blond, with hair perfectly combed, his physique was one that had once been very athletic and was still powerful and his nice-looking, young-success face seemed immobile, as though he was preoccupied with incorruptibility and efficiency.

He identified himself as a sergeant of the department's Internal Affairs Division and leaned forward over his desk so that Stiver had to leave his seat to shake the extended hand.

"I've looked into the incident you and Professor . . . " he looked up.

"Rowland."

"Yes. Rowland seemed to have a complaint about and found there seems to be no grounds for any action by the department." His face was bland, inoffensive.

David blinked. This was the fastest attempted brush-off he'd ever heard of.

"I don't understand. This was concerning the arrest the other night of two men in East Los Angeles . . ."

The sergeant picked up a folder. "Yes. I have all the facts here. You seemed to think there was some misconduct on the part of the officers . . ."

"I don't seem to think anything. I was there. I saw police in battle helmets with shotguns pointed at people, one of them deliberately bumped a man, then they beat him and . . ."

"Hold on a second," the sergeant said quietly, pressing a

buzzer. In a moment a voice answered. "Ask Jack to come in, will you please?" He didn't wait for an answer. "Being quite truthful with you, I personally didn't interrogate the officers involved . . . "

"Why didn't you?"

"Because I have assistants who are quite able. I read all the reports concerning the matter, including the report by Jack Flowers, who will be here in a second. He talked to the officers involved."

The door at the rear, through which the sergeant had entered, opened and a well-shaped, handsome Negro of perhaps thirty entered. He wore a dark stylish suit and his hair was well cropped. He nodded to the sergeant and looked with friendly interest at Stiver.

"Jack," the sergeant said, "this is Mr. Stiver. Mr. Stiver, this is Officer Jack Flowers, also of the Internal Affairs Division. He questioned the officers involved."

Jack Flowers smiled broadly as he stepped to David and extended his hand.

"Glad to meet you, Mr. Stiver," he said. His face still held friendly interest.

"The same," Stiver said.

The sergeant continued. "Mr. Stiver had a complaint about the case. That's why we put you on it, Jack." To Stiver, "We look into every reported incident of misconduct that comes to our attention."

Jack Flowers: "Yes, a department can never be sure when it has a bad apple or two, so we check out every story." He smiled broadly. "It's a lot of leg work, but that's what we're here for."

Stiver realized that, except for a few traffic citations, he had never come in contact with a policeman. Well, by God, I'm not afraid to speak up, he told himself.

"The sergeant here just informed me that an investigation revealed no evidence of any misconduct by a policeman in that arrest on the east side the other night," Stiver said confidently.

The sergeant cut in quickly, "I never said we had an investigation. I said we looked into it."

"Well, whatever you call it, then. Anyway, I have here the newspaper clipping of the incident . . . " He pulled out the clipping and read, " 'CROWD TRIES TO TAKE PRISONERS—A crowd of more than one hundred persons attempted to take two prisoners from police custody in East

Los Angeles last night' . . . " He put down the clipping.
"This report isn't true. This is your version of . . . "

The sergeant spoke: "We have no control—nor do we
want any—over the free press. What the paper prints is
none of our . . . "

"Then how did they get this information? There was no
newspaperman present when this happened."

Flowers smiled. "How do you know there wasn't?"

"Because I was there, that's how." Flowers was only
momentarily chagrined. "But I want to know, if this isn't
your version, whose is it?"

"Our police blotter is open to representatives of the free
press. We have no right, under ordinary conditions, to with-
hold information of public interest—nor do we want to."
The sergeant had a particular manner he used when re-
peating this last phrase, David noted.

"Well, then, it *is* just your version."

"If you have differences with the reporting done by the
newspaper, you should take it up with them," the sergeant
said politely.

"Now wait a minute. Wait a minute. Let's don't get side-
tracked by this newspaper business. The other night I saw
the most flagrant example of atrocious behavior imaginable
by police. I saw a mob of friendly people threatened with
shotguns, a man tricked into seemingly knocking down an
officer . . . "

Flowers cut in, "The officer said the man tried to knock
him down. He arrested him for assaulting a police officer
and interfering with an arrest."

"Assaulting a police officer my ass!" Stiver was becoming
angry. He noted the policemen showed no sign of annoyance. "That's the phoniest thing I ever heard of!"

"That's not what the officer involved claims, or more than
a dozen others who saw it, claim."

"Then they're lying!"

The sergeant spoke quietly: "Then you're suggesting that
the officers who filed their reports of that incident were
deliberately falsifying the evidence?"

"If that's what they all said, yes. They were lying through
their teeth."

Officer Flowers looked serious. "If what you say is true,
then this is corruption among the police of this department
—this falsifying of evidence."

"All right, then. It's corruption. But I know what I saw."

"You know, I know Doc Howell out there at the university. He's head of Police Sciences."

"I know him too," Stiver snapped.

"Well," the sergeant's tone was a tiny bit menacing, "according to many surveys and many reports by independent, non-vested interest groups, the Los Angeles Police Department enjoys the most corruption-free personnel of any Police Department in the nation."

"That's a well-known fact," Officer Flowers put in. "Doc Howell out there could verify that."

"And here you are trying to tell us just the opposite is true. That a dozen policemen will conspire to falsify evidence—and that's a felony, by the way—and do it without any motive of personal gain. I don't see how you expect us to believe we have that kind of policemen, when even the *Reader's Digest* in at least two different articles has pointed out the non-corruptibility of our force," the sergeant said reasonably.

"Yes, I know all about that. But I'm beginning to see some things a little differently now. I'm telling you, charging that man with assaulting an officer is the most hideous thing . . . "

"Incidentally," the sergeant put in quietly, "although the charge could have been made to stick, it was dropped. Even though many police officers at the scene were ready to swear he assaulted the officer."

Flowers took over, "We have a policy of, when a suspect becomes unreasonable and infracts too many statutes, trying to drop as many of the more serious charges against him. We're not out to persecute anyone. That man was originally charged with assaulting an officer, resisting arrest, interfering with an arrest and drunk. All but the last charge was dropped."

Stiver was a little at a loss.

"I'd like to be able to say that was nice of you, but the thing was phony from the beginning. You police were out to get somebody. Just because of the area . . . "

In the presence of Officer Flowers, Stiver realized how weak an accusation of discrimination would sound. He was a little confused, unsure.

"If we want to 'get somebody,' as you put it, would we have dropped all the serious charges against this man?"

"You might have, knowing you couldn't make it stick . . . "

Flowers, smiling, "Believe, Mr. Stiver. With more than a dozen witnesses, all completely incorruptible, all veteran officers with good records, those charges could be made to stick. I know. I don't know how much you've been around courtroom procedure, but . . . "

Stiver was aware his mounting anger put him at a disadvantage among cooler heads. "Wait 'til this comes to court. He'll have fifty witnesses that he wasn't even drunk. They'll all fight this frameup . . ." Too late, he saw a look of gratification, triumph, in their eyes.

The sergeant spoke as quietly as ever, "Evidently you didn't know the two men taken that night went to court this morning and pleaded guilty to drunk and disturbing the peace and drunk."

Stiver sat, silenced. "No. I didn't know that," he said finally.

"Well, you see, this is what happens when you don't understand these things. Now if either of those men had any complaints about an injustice being inflicted on them, they certainly wouldn't have pleaded guilty. To anything. I know *I* wouldn't. Would you, Officer Flowers?"

Flowers smiled genially. "I sure wouldn't. There's no power in the world that can force you to make a confession against your will in *this* country. You think we used the 'third degree'?"

Stiver was exasperated. He sat back, pushing a hand through his hair, not knowing where to start again.

"All right, now listen. I'm getting nowhere. I'm a resident of this town. I want satisfaction. I think you've done a lousy job of looking into this thing. I think your eyes are closed to any misconduct."

The sergeant picked up a printed pamphlet.

"We make regular reports on this sort of thing. For the city. It's all a matter of public record, including the fact that fifty per cent of all brutality charges investigated by the Police Department are confirmed, and action is taken. Do you believe that?"

Stiver hesitated. The sergeant held what he knew was proof of what he had just said in his hand, waiting.

Officer Flower took it up. "And fifty per cent confirmation by a department is probably the highest rate in the country. Does that sound like we're trying to conceal misconduct or brutality?"

"No . . . I guess it doesn't. But I'm not so sure you've

really investigated this to the fullest extent . . ." He noticed the sergeant and Officer Flowers glance fleetingly at one another. He concentrated. "But wait . . . you say half of all cases investigated are confirmed and action taken?"

"That's right. No other department . . . "

Stiver cut in. "But when I first came in, you, sergeant, made it a point to point out you didn't say this incident was investigated, didn't you?"

The police officers looked at each other.

"Is that the catch? In that report to the citizens there? 'Fifty per cent of all cases *investigated*.' That's what you mean, isn't it?"

Neither answered. Stiver continued. "All right, tell me this. Is this incident we're talking about going into the record as one you've investigated?"

He waited. They looked at him. "I'm waiting for an answer, Sergeant."

Impatiently, "Look, Mr. Stiver. We're very busy. I told you we looked into this and found there's nothing to investigate."

"How do I know you looked into it?"

The sergeant smiled. "You'll just have to take my word for it. If you think we're going to pull fifteen men out of the field just to interrogate them in front of you, you're mistaken. This thing has been handled in the usual manner."

"Okay. Then tell me who decides whether a case warrants 'investigation' or not. Tell me who, and I'll go see him. I'm wasting my time here."

"You're also wasting our time, Mr. Stiver. If you don't like the way this police department is run, go see City Hall."

"I did. They sent me here saying you handle this sort of thing. Are you the one who decides whether an incident gets investigated or not?"

"Yes, I am." Angrily.

Stiver stood silent by his chair. "I see. A dead end, eh? And what about those people," he pointed, "out there? Who do they go to if they think they've been abused?"

The sergeant's composure had returned. "If they have a legitimate complaint it's handled through the proper channels."

"And what are the proper channels?"

Mildly, "Though this office. We'll hear any complaint and take some action."

"Even if that action is a decision to take no action or not

investigate." It wasn't a question. The sergeant shrugged.

"Look, kid. Your old man may be a big shot back east, but don't think you can come here and tell us . . ."

"What do you mean about my old man?"

They looked at him, inscrutable. "Tell me," he continued, "what do you know about me? Good God! Since yesterday you've already had me checked out?" He looked at them, demanding. "Answer me! You've investigated me? Tell me, what'd you come up with? Did you find out I played hooky twice in the seventh grade?"

They just stared. "You didn't think the facts in this case warranted an investigation. But you had me checked out two thousand miles away."

His fury at being checked out was apparent, and as he turned to go neither policeman gave a parting word or gesture. At the door he turned back and looked at them. They remained motionless, awaiting his departure, faces blank. He looked hard at the sergeant first, then at Officer Flowers.

"Shit!" he said and walked out.

He dozed, awakening slowly. The afternoon sunlight streamed in between the nearly closed drapes of the window on the west wall of his bedroom. She was up and hadn't noticed he was awake, watching her. *Mariana, Mariana,* he said to himself as he watched her pull the simple cotton capris over her softly full hips and rump and then pull on her loose jersey. Her leather sandals seemed to put themselves on her feet and then she was in front of the mirror, stroking her shoulder-length black hair with the brush she now kept in his dresser drawer. Odd, he thought, how with other girls, afterward it was always an effort to keep from saying, "Okay, now get away from me and leave me alone." And now he wanted to get up and talk to her, listen to what she had to say, enjoy being the object of her attention. Now she was straightening things, putting books on the shelf, hanging a sweater or jacket in his closet. She suddenly saw something on the closet floor and stooped to pick it up. She looked at him and saw he was awake.

"David! Is that what you did with this cowhide I brought you? Just threw it on the closet floor?"

He sat up and stretched. "Honest, I haven't had time to find a place to hang it. I really like it, old as it is."

"That's the beauty of it. It looks like it came from another century, and it did."

"Is that the one I saw at your grandfather's?"

"Not the same one. He had two. There's evidently a real story behind them. He told me his father—my greatgrandfather, had many when they decided to come here, and the family traded them off for food and shelter on the way. Only two were left and he gave me one. And I gave it to you and you threw it on the floor in your closet."

"I'm sorry," he said, sitting on the edge of the bed.

"It belongs on the couch in the living room," she said walking out of the bedroom. "Come on, get up. We've got to have this place ready for your mother and father. They'll be arriving in a few hours, you know."

When he walked into the living room, dressed, she was emptying ashtrays, stuffing old newspapers and magazines into a wastebasket. She held up a clipping that had been on a table. "You want to save the newspaper clipping about the arrests . . . that night?"

He suddenly seemed weary. "Yes, I suppose so. That seems to be the only thing to show for my efforts." He gave her a little despairing smile, "I'm sorry I failed you, Mariana. But I tried. For two months now. But the newspapers say it's dead copy, too old now. And nobody else will listen. Or else they send me back to that sergeant."

She came to him and put her hands on his face. He put his arms around her, his hands running up and far down her back. "You tried, David. As hard as you could. That's all anyone can do. And I love you more for it. And I intend to tell your mother and father about what a shining knight you've turned out to be."

He turned away. "Oh, I wouldn't do that just yet," he said, evasiveness creeping into his attitude. "Besides . . . I guess my mother's not . . . going to be on the plane."

She had turned back to her work but now she stopped. "Your mother's not coming? How come?"

"Well, I guess she had . . . lots of things to do. She's awfully busy, you know, and after all, this was originally just a business trip for Dad. And I suggested they make it a visit. But Marge is coming. You'll love her, Mariana. She's really tops."

"Yes, you've told me all about her. But your mother. I'm really sorry she couldn't come. You did tell her about me when you went home last month, didn't you?"

"Yes, of course I did."

"Well, I'm disappointed she can't come. I . . ."

"Mariana," with a little irritation, "it's not like we were engaged . . . or something . . ."

She looked at him, then lowered her eyes to the floor, nodding slightly. "Yes, David, you're right. It's not like we were going to be married . . . or something."

He stepped to her and pulled her into his arms. "Now look here. There's no reason for you to feel . . . like you're feeling. It's not at all like you think . . ."

She gazed with wistful intensity into his face, and her voice was soft. "You really have a good thing going, don't you, David?" And she twisted away. He caught her.

"Mariana, we've never had a quarrel yet. Let's don't start. Dad and Marge will be here soon. Let's show them a good time."

As she looked up at him the serious lines left her face and a smile, only slightly forced, came. She hugged his chest suddenly. "Sure," she said cheerily, "come on, now. There's just time for me to pick up this place while you make us a snack, then you've got to run me home while I change and then we're off to the airport."

As he fixed sandwiches in the kitchen he called to her, "You're not nervous at all over meeting Dad and Marge, are you?"

She called back, "There's no reason I should be," and she waited just the right length of time, ". . . is there, David." It was not a question, and her tone made him feel miserable.

Stiver wondered how it looked to Mariana as he shook hands with his father and pecked his sister on the cheek at the airport. Here it is, he thought. Here what is? Had he really brought them together just for his own amusement? No, he hadn't, he reasoned. He was watching for their reaction when they realized the cream-colored girl was the one he was with. He noticed the eyes of both of them caught Mariana and held firmly as they turned to meet her. What were they expecting anyway . . .

Keen interest, admiration, friendliness, he saw in his sister and father as he introduced each. Mariana stood tall, as she always did, her shyness scantily clad, her lips clipping her words to give them that trace of accent which conveyed the fact that she was crossing a gap to meet on their terms. Only when she smiled was it evident she was not yet out of her teens.

David's father, doing his best not to be a typical father, or a typical successful businessman, or a typical anything, was remarkably unobnoxious, David thought affectionately as Mr. Stiver mumbled something about being very pleased and charmed to meet Mariana. Marge was a good deal more original, genuine, with, "Honestly, how does a girl who looks like you, expect a woman my age to like you!" Then Marge laughed. Good girl, David thought, she could make even the most reluctant cynic like her almost immediately.

Mariana and Marge followed as the four rode the conveyor toward the street entrance to the building. David heard Marge rattling on, ". . . closer to thirty than I am to twenty and don't give me that 'you don't look it' stuff."

His father, ". . . hope you're as hungry as I am, I can never eat much on a plane. Let's go to that hotel out on Sunset . . ."

They sat in the dark dining room, Mr. Stiver trying to crack the shell of his lobster quietly, Marge savoring her large salad, David and Mariana picked at their food.

"I'm glad you were able to come out here with your father," Mariana said to Marge. Marge finished a mouthful.

"Well, actually, Dad's afraid to leave me behind. He thinks I might get married again. He lives in dread of having an oft-married daughter on his hands."

"Marge!" Mr. Stiver said with polite annoyance. "You make it sound like you'd been married a half dozen times, instead of just once."

"Once and a half," she shot back. Then to Mariana: "I'm the family skeleton. An old divorcée at twenty-five. Dad drove my first husband away," she turned to him. "Thank you, Dad, by the way." She kissed two fingers and patted them on his lips.

"Marge, please don't say your 'first husband.' It sounds . . ."

"Well he was my first husband. That doesn't necessarily mean I've had others, just that he won't be my last. I hope. So do you."

"And as for my driving him away . . ."

Marge interrupted. "Yes, that is unfair of me. Dad really didn't. My husband became disenchanted when he found out he was expected to work at the sales management job Dad gave him."

Mariana laughed a little uncomfortably.

David spoke to her. "Mariana, one thing I must tell you. Marge thinks it's chic . . . or . . . sophisticated to speak openly about family affairs. I . . ."

"Oh, for Christ sake, David, quit apologizing for me. I don't think anything of the sort. If I hide something, then

I'm an inhibited Puritan. If I don't, then I'm trying to be sophisticated. I just don't give a darn."

Mr. Stiver spoke next. "Mariana, you're a native of these parts?"

"Yes. I was born in . . . Los Angeles. My mother too. We're what you call natives, I guess."

"What is your father in?"

"He does construction work. I don't really know much about what he does."

Marge looked up from her salad. "By the way, Dad, what do you do?"

He looked a little annoyed. Marge laughed.

"Really, Mariana, I know what he does. But I don't know *how* he does it. He owns a company that sells class. For the mass. Company motto: Class delivered to your door."

Mariana smiled at Mr. Stiver. "Sounds interesting."

"Hell of it is, she's right. I have a door-to-door sales business. It's unique. At least I think it is, even though my son and daughter think it's funny . . ."

David cut in: "Dad! I don't think it's humorous. I never said . . ."

"I do," Marge said. "I think it's a riot. Dad has hundreds of salesmen going door to door, selling Rembrandt copies, prints of wall drawings of primitive man, lamps made out of Early American butter churns or spinning wheels, which he had made in Japan, incidentally. He even sells antique electric clocks, can you imagine."

Mr. Stiver was smilling. "And all this seems atrocious to my offspring, but not to me. When I started this business, a long time ago by the way, I felt I was filling a great need. I still feel that way. The people my men call on would ordinarily never buy anthing like . . . like the things Marge just mentioned. No one ever before brought items of culture to the front door of Mr. and Mrs. John Q."

"With nothing down, ninety days to pay," Marge footnoted. "But Dad, please don't call them items of culture. This girl here probably has more artistic-ness in her little finger than we all have put together. She'd get a big laugh out of one of your Aztec calendars which you have carved in Spain out of imitation Italian marble."

"That's not true," Mariana said earnestly. "I know nothing about art. I think if you can offer facsimiles of masterpieces you are filling a great need. Even if they are mass produced."

Mr. Stiver beamed. "Thank you, Miss Sando . . . I know you'll forgive me being unable to say your name."

"Sando-*val*," Mariana said. "Accent on the last syllable." She said the name with an explosive "ball" on the end.

Marge mused. "If I could develop an accent like you have I'd drive 'em crazy. You don't have a brother, do you?"

"Yes."

Marge brightened. "How old is he?"

David was only half listening to the patter. He thought of Sammy. And then of Sammy with Marge. And he saw, nothing to do with age difference, how ridiculous it was. Was he missing the ridiculousness of himself and Mariana somehow? As they talked he tried to picture her ten years hence in Illinois.

He couldn't make the picture come. She didn't fit. All right then, in East L.A. Yes, in a kitchen apron, dark children crawling on the floor, men like her father in steel helmets talking loudly as she served chili, warmed a bottle, poured wine, her jet hair perhaps in a kerchief, laughing and talking as shrilly as her gentle voice could to compete with the loud voices and the crying, tripping over a large dog lying in the middle of the kitchen floor, as oblivious to the goings-on as the other people. He imagined he could see the strength born in Mariana, a strength perhaps the result of a heritage of resignation, that could enable her to go through any amount of physical discomfort or hardship. He could see, comparing his sister to her, that it would kill Marge to live in a two-room East. L.A. shack for twenty years. And it would kill Mariana to find social rejection in Illinois, whereas Marge spat at the mention of rejection by his mother's social circle.

He was dragged back: ". . . Father hates sociology . . . don't butt in, Dad, you do too—I'm talking to her. You know, some kids, to spite their folks, turn hippie, or take dope. David takes sociology," she slowed to take a bite of food and added, "Some become divorcées . . ."

David saw the reason and logic for the seemingly senseless chatter Marge put out. The poor girl, he thought. Always desperately trying to help someone. She was trying to give Mariana a good family picture, let her really see the Stivers as they were, phony, yes, but real people too. Marge always tried to make things appear as they really were.

Mariana began making those almost imperceptible motions that mean a woman is ready to leave. "Really, I have things to do, David. I know you'd like to visit more with your sister right now, so why don't you let your father drop me off. I'd like a chance to talk to him." David agreed and gave the keys to his father.

"Nothing short of driving with a girl like you could make me face the Los Angeles freeways and smog," Mr. Stiver said sincerely.

She gave Mr. Stiver instructions and they drove silently for some minutes. She looked at him. "I guess it's an old, old story, isn't it?" and tears came as she suddenly bowed her head.

He nodded, eyes on the road, but his face suddenly showed lines that hadn't been there before. After a long pause, "I guess no father should ever be shocked. If he raises a son to manhood. Does David know?"

"No. And I won't let him, if it means he thinks it'll wreck his life." She looked up, blinking with determination.

"But he should. What about your parents?"

She thought a minute before answering. "I don't suppose you'd understand this, but they feel . . . it's kind of a custom to believe, that when a girl gets pregnant it's only her fault. Every man has the right to try to seduce every girl he can. And he should be responsible for a child only if it's his wife who has a baby."

Mr. Stiver nodded. "European style, sort of. But what are you going to do?"

She shrugged. "That's up to David. I'll find out how he feels, and if it will upset his life's plans, I'll just stay home with Mom and Dad and have the child. I won't be the first this has happened to. Or the ten-thousandth."

"But . . . you don't understand, Mariana. It's different, in a way. The law says that as long as David has a child anywhere he is responsible for that child . . ."

"Yes, I know. Among us . . . my people, an illegitimate child is another kid to have around. But in David's world it would make the difference in whether a certain family would allow him to marry a daughter, or whether he was socially acceptable or not, or whether Mr. Richpants would make him a superintendent of a factory. Mr. Stiver, as David's pregnant girlfriend, I represent a threat to him bigger than anything in the world. I don't think he wants to get married to anybody, maybe especially me. And when he knows I'm having his baby I'll be like a cannonball tied to his leg. He'll hate me. There's not the slightest doubt in my mind that I've lost him. Maybe I have a few more weeks, a month or two maybe, to be the girl in his life. That's all."

He looked at her and saw a pride and strength he'd never seen in anyone else.

"Then what will you do?"

She smiled, not a sad smile. "I'll stay home with Mom and Dad. Like I said, it isn't the first time this ever happened."

They rode silently again for a time. Then he said, "Mariana, I want you to know . . . that I'm positive . . . there's no doubt it could only be David's."

She put her hand on his on the steering wheel. "Thank you," she said softly with a soft smile.

He drove, looking straight ahead. Then, "I don't know where I failed . . ."

"You didn't! It's not your fault things are the way they are. You can't be blamed for anything."

"But . . . then, how, what can I do? How can I help . . . ?"

"There's no way you can help. There's nothing you can do. Except maybe learn that there are some things you can't do anything about. David wouldn't accept any help from you. Or advice. You getting involved in this would only make you two be further apart."

He dropped her off, assuring her he knew how to get to David's apartment, making her promise she'd come see them off at the airport. He asked to come in to meet her parents and she looked at him, shaking her head, and said, "Why?"

David wanted to walk the ten blocks to his apartment, but Marge insisted on a cab. As he let her in and, without asking, began to make her a highball, she looked around.

"Not a half bad place. Dad keeps you in pretty good style, I'd say."

"You don't do bad by him yourself," David answered.

She took the drink and sat down. "She's a lovely person, David. You're in love with her, aren't you?"

He seemed to become irritable. "I think she's the greatest. Sweet girl, and all that."

Marge looked at him fondly. "Dearest brother. How do you get in these . . . ?"

"These what? For chrissake, I'm not in anything. I just have a beautiful Latin girlfriend."

"Fine. Okay. You're not in anything. Just in love with an adorable Mexican girl, that's all. Why don't you take her home to Mama, like you did that Coulter bitch last year? Mom thought she was the greatest."

He went to the kitchen and poured himself one, talking as he did. "Mom, you know her, doesn't understand everything. But if I felt like it, I would. If I wanted to marry this girl, nothing would stop me." He returned and took a seat.

"My ass, nothing would stop you."

Stiver laughed a little. "You know, you're the only attractive babe I ever knew who could say vulgar things and remain just as attractive. If Mariana ever said that . . . " His voice trailed off.

She sipped and looked knowingly at him. "That's how it is, huh? Mariana this, Mariana that. You know, David, I envy you tremendously, being able to fall in love. I can't. I go with or marry whatever man is the least repugnant."

He remained silent, thinking a moment. "Maybe you're right, Marge. But it doesn't matter. Mom and Dad have done too good a job on us. We have to fit in where our nests are made back home. Even you, who think you haven't fit in well, are acting out the part written for you. Things are the way they are and they don't change. You don't know about Mariana. It's an entirely different world. The fact that Mom would have a breakdown if I brought her home doesn't really make much difference. It's a million other things that would make life too complicated with her. And our life with our phony standards and values is complex enough without taking on a lifetime project of reshaping round holes to fit square pegs. I guess I love Mariana, but it will be over soon and that'll be the end of it. It can't be any other way."

"Attaboy, Davey. You always were made out of the stuff that knuckles under."

He looked at her sharply. "Don't get bitchy with me, Marge."

"I'll get bitchy with anybody I please. God! If I'd ever had something going with somebody outside our rat-race, how quick I would have chucked it all."

"That's easy to say, but nothing's ever stopped you. You love the way things are for us. You snub the tennis set and all that, but you really belong to the class Dad's money put us in."

"Tell me, David. When you started out as a sociology major, did you ever really plan to get your degree and then go out and become a five-hundred-dollar-a-month social worker? Or go with the Peace Corps?"

He was downcast. "No. I always knew I'd go to Dad and say, 'Okay, I'll take your area superintendent job.' I was just having a rebellious fling. But it's different now. I plan to go into Dad's business—some day I'll run it for him—and I'll implement a hundred ideas I have about equal opportunity employment, advancement. Really, I . . ."

"David, if bullshit was music you'd be a symphony orchestra. So this is how you rationalize not having the courage to marry the girl you love. You're trying to tell yourself you're making a great sacrifice so that later you can be in a position to make changes. Good Christ! I've really heard it all now. At least I hoped you would have some original excuse for being afraid to face up to Mother."

He felt his face grow red from the smart of truth. He remembered how it had been when he'd flown home for spring vacation. In grand style he'd broken the news he was going with "a fine Mexican girl," then realized such a statement conformed to the consensus that all Mexican girls weren't necessarily fine.

He recalled with a twinge of bitterness the conversation with his mother. She was about to leave the house to attend a meeting. As always, she was dressed rather conservatively but stylish, her clothes worn to emphasize subtly her still-in-the-thirties look, although she readily admitted to being several years older.

"David, I really would love to meet your little Spanish girl, in spite of the fact you think I'm . . . " She paused at his look of acute irritation, "What's the matter, dear? Now what'd I say?"

David thought a moment, then put his finger on it.

"She's not little. What makes you think she's little? She's five feet six. Taller than you."

"I . . . did I say she was little? I certainly didn't mean to. But now that you call me on *that,* I understand these people are smaller than . . . well, than the average. Aren't they?"

"Maybe yes, maybe no. Perhaps they were a generation ago. But she's not. No, Mother, funny I'd never heard the slur in such an innocent sounding thing as 'little Spanish girl,' but it's there."

Now his mother looked exasperated. "David! Good grief. There is no slur in what I said. 'Little Spanish girl' is just

. . . an expression, that's all. Is that more of what sociology has taught you?"

"No, Mother. What you really meant is, let's see . . . insignificant. Yes. You had no reason to know or care how big she is. 'Little Spanish girl' is an expression of contempt, whether you realize it or not. It has nothing to do with how tall you think she is. And she's Mexican. Not Spanish." Mrs. Stiver thought a moment. "I was just being kind when I said 'Spanish,' David. I'm sure she's a lovely girl, and she wouldn't appreciate being called Mexican . . ." She stopped as she saw David's complete attitude of exasperation. "We can't even talk to each other hardly any more, can we, David?"

David looked straight at her. "Hardly."

"I guess we don't understand one another."

There was a little pause before he answered. "I understand you, Mother," and she had left to attend a meeting of the volunteer workers for her church group's Project Ghetto.

God! What a disaster that had been, his attempt to reach his mother. He now sat looking at Marge. She looked at him. And suddenly they both smiled.

"Look," she said with spirit. "Dad and I are on a visit here, and we're sitting here talking about miserable life. We only have tonight and tomorrow, so let's liven things up and quit commiserating."

A knock sounded at the door. David rose. "Ah, Dad's found his way back. He promised us a big night out on him. Let's get going."

They sat, the three of them, watching a floorshow after dinner. Marge danced and flirted. David watched and laughed. Mr. Stiver studied his two children and said little. Toward the end of the evening Marge looked at him. "Dad! What's the matter? You look like you're almost crying."

He cleared his head, knowing he had drunk a little too much.

"I'm . . . so inadequate," he murmured, and then laughed at the floorshow. They didn't hear him.

from *The Plum Plum Pickers*

Raymond Barrio

Dawn.

Outside, the coolest night.

Outside, the soft, plush, lingering sheen of nightlight.

Within his breezy airconditioned shack Manuel lay half asleep in the middle of the biggest apricot orchard in the world, nothing but apricot trees all around, in one of a long double row of splintered boards nailed together and called a shack. A migrant's shack. He struggled to come awake. Everything seemed to be plugged up. A distant roar closed in steadily. He awoke in a cold sweat. He sat up abruptly in the cold darkness.

The roar grew louder and louder. He leaned forward, hunched in his worn, torn covers, and peered through the grimy window. A huge black monster was butting through trees, moving and pitching about, its headlights piercing the armor of night, then swinging away again as the roaring lessened. Manuel smiled. The roar of a tractor. He rubbed the sleep from his eyes. He stretched his aching arms and shoulders. He thought of Lupe and the kids back in Drawbridge.

On the very brink of the full onslaught of summer's punishing heat, with the plums and pears and apricots fattening madly on every vine, branch, bush and limb in every section of every county in the country, pickers were needed right now immediately on every farm and orchard everywhere and all at once. The frantic demand for pickers increased rapidly as the hot days mounted. That sure looked good out there. What a cool job that was. Driving a tractor at night. Maybe he could get Ramiro to teach him to drive one.

Manuel well knew what his physical energy was.

His physical energy was his total worldly wealth.

No matter how anxious he was to work, he did have his limit. He had to rest his body. The finger joint he'd injured still hurt. He missed Lupe's chatter. He'd signed up with that shrewd contractor, Roberto Morales, that shrewd, fat, energetic contratista, manipulator of migrating farm workers, that smiling middleman who promised to deliver so many hands to the moon at such and such a time at such and such an orchard at such and such a price, for such a small commission. A tiny percentage. Such a little slice. Silvery slavery—modernized.

Roberto Morales, an organization man, was a built-in toll gate. A parasite. A collector of drops of human sweat. An efficiency expert. Had he had not been Mexican, he would have made a fantastic capitalist, like Turner. He was Turner upside down. Sucking blood from his own people. With the help and convenient connivance of Turner's insatiable greed.

The agricultural combine's imperative need to have its capital personally plucked when ripe so as to materialize its honest return on its critical investment in order to keep its executives relaxed in blue splendor in far-off desert pools, was coupled to the migrant workers' inexorable and uncompromising need to earn pennies to fend off stark starvation.

Good money.

Good dough.

Good hard work.

Pick fast.

Penny a bucket.

Check off.

Get the count right.

Cotsplumsprunespeachesbeanspeas.

Pods.

The seed of life.

And:—don't complain. . . .

Manuel lay back in the blackness. As the darkness receded and the light of day started creeping imperiously across its own land, he thought that these powerful orchard land owners were awfully generous to give him such a beautiful hostel to stop in overnight. The skylight hotel. There the land stood. A heaving, sleeping mother earth. A marvelous land. Ripening her fruit once again. Once more. Ripening it fatly and pregnantly for the thousandth time. It must be plucked said the wise man. For it cannot hang around on limbs a minute extra. At no man's convenience. As soon as the baby's ready. Lush and full of plump juices. Hugging its new seed around its own ripeness. The plum and the cot and the peach and the pear must plummet again to earth. Carrying the seed of its own delicate rebirth and redestruction back home to earth again. A clever mother earth who in her all-but-unbelievable generosity was capable of giving man fivefold, tenfold the quantity of fruit he could himself eat, five times fifty, and yet the pickers were never paid enough to satisfy their hunger beyond their actual working hours. And yet it was called a moral world. An ethical world. A good world. A happy world. A world full of golden opportunities. Manuel simply couldn't figure it out.

What was wrong with the figures?

Why was mother earth so generous? And men so greedy?

You got twenty-five cents a basket for tomatoes. A dollar a crate for some fruit. You had to work fast. That was the whole thing. A frantic lunatic to make your barely living wage. If you had no rent to pay, it was OK. You were ahead, amigo. Pay rent, however, stay in one place, and you couldn't migrate after other easy pickings. The joy of working was looking over your dreams locked to hunger.

Manuel studied the whorls in the woodwork whirling slowly, revealed in the faint crepuscular light penetrating his shack. His cot was a slab of half-inch plywood board twenty-two inches wide and eight feet long, the width of the shack, supported by two two-by-four beams butted up against the wall at both ends beneath the side window. The shack itself was eight by twelve by seven feet high. Its roof had a slight pitch. The rain stains in the ceiling planks revealed the ease with which the rain penetrated. Except for two small panes of glass exposed near the top, most of the window at the opposite end was boarded up. A single, old, paint-encrusted door was the only entry. No curtains. No interior paneling. Just a shack. A shack of misery. He found he was able to admire and appreciate the simplicity and the strength of the construction. He counted the upright studs, level, two feet apart, the double joists across the top supporting the roof. Cracks and knotholes aplenty, in the wall siding, let in bright chinks of light during the day and welcome wisps of clear fresh air at night. The rough planking of the siding was stained dark. The floor was only partly covered with odd sections of plywood. Some of the rough planking below was exposed, revealing cracks leading down to the cool black earth beneath. A small thick table was firmly studded to a portion of the wall opposite the door. A few small pieces of clear lumber stood bunched together,

unsung, unused, unhurried, in the far corner. An overhead
shelf, supported from the ceiling by a small extending
perpendicular arm, containing some boxes of left-over chem-
icals and fertilizers, completed the furnishings in his temporary abode.

It was habitable.

He could raise his family in it.

If they were rabbits.

The first rays of a brute new day clinked in through the
small rectangle of panes. The ray hovered, then peaked,
then rested on the covers pushed up by his knees. He recalled his mountain trips with his uncle to the great forbid-
ding barrancas near Durango in Central Mexico, and
stopping to rest in the middle of the wild woods, and coming
unexpectedly upon a crumbling, splintered hulk of a shack
that was all falling apart. It barely gave them shelter from
the sudden pelting storm they were trying to escape, he as
a young frightened boy, but shelter it was—and how beautiful that experience was, then, for they were free, daring,
adventurers, out there in that wilderness, alone and daring,
with nothing between them and God's own overpowering
nature, alone. They belonged to nothing. To no one. But
themselves. They were dignity purified. No one forced them
to go or stay there. They were delighted and grateful to the
shack. For the protection it afforded them. Though it was
hardly more than a ratty pile of splinters. Far worse than
this one he was now occupying . . . but also somehow
far more beautiful in his memory.

And now. Here he was. Shut up in this miserable shack.
So sturdily built. Thinking how it sickened him inside because it was more a jail cell than a shelter. He didn't care
how comfortable and convenient the growers made the
shacks for him. They were huts of slavery. What he wanted
was an outlet for his pride. A sudden fierce wave of anger
made him want to cross the shack with his fists. There had
to be some way to cross the ungulfable bridge. Why was
necessity always the bride of hunger? To be free . . . ah,
and also to be able to eat all one wanted. My heart, mi
corazón, why did work always have to blend with such
misery? The welcome warmth of the sun's early rays, penetrating more, warmed his frame. But it was a false, false
hope. He knew it. The work that lay ahead of him that day
would drain and stupify and fatigue him once again to the
point of senseless torpor, ready to fall over long before the

work day was done. And that fatigue wasn't nearly so bad
to bear as the deadly repetitious monotony of never changing, never resting, doing the same plucking over and over
and over again. But he had to do it. He had no choice. It
was all he could do. It had to be done if he wanted the
money. And he had to have the money, if he wanted to
feed his family. The brain in his arms was his only capital.
Not very much, true, but it was the only sacrifice he could
offer the money gods, the only heart he could offer on the
pyramid of gold.

His life. La gran vida.

Wide awake now, fully refreshed, his whole body lithe
and toned, Manuel was ashamed to find himself eager to
start in work, knowing that he would do well, but ashamed
because he could think of nothing he would rather do more.
The final step.

The final the final the final the final the final the final
step.

To want to work oneself to death. A la muerte. It wasn't
the work itself that bothered him. It was the total immer-
sion, the endless, ceaseless, total use of all his energies and
spirit and mind and being that tore him apart within. He
didn't know what else he was good for or could do with his
life. But there had to be something else. He had to be something more than a miserable plucking animal. Pluck pluck
pluck. Feed feed feed. Glug glug glug. Dressing quickly,
rolling up his blanket roll and stuffing it into a corner to
use again that night, Manuel stepped coolly out into the
morning sweetness and breathed the honeyscented humidity
rinsing air rising from the honied soil, and joined the thick-
ening throng of his fellow pluckers milling about the large
open barn serving as a cookout. Feeding all the pickers was
another of the fat man's unholy prerogatives, for he cheated
and overpriced on meals too. Roberto Morales, the fat man,
the shrewd contratista, was a bully man, busily darting his
blob about, exhorting his priceless pickers to hurry, answering questions, giving advice, in the cool half-light, impatiently, pushing, giving orders. Manuel, in order to avoid
having to greet him, scowled at his toes when Roberto came
trouncing by, saying, "Apúrense, compañeros, hurry, hurry,
hurry, amigos." Sure. Amigos. Sí. Sí. Frens. They all gulped
their food down hurriedly, standing. Just like home. Paper
plates, plastic cups. Wooden spoons. And bits of garbage
flying into large canisters. Then in the still cool nightlike

morning air, like a flood of disturbed birds, they all picked up their pails and filed into the orchard.

The apricots were plump.

Smooth.

A golden syrupy orange.

Manuel popped two into his mouth, enjoying their cool natural sweetness after the bitter coffee. He knew he could not eat too many. His stomach muscles would cramp. Other pickers started pulling rapidly away from him. Let them. Calmly he calculated the struggle. Start the press sure, slow, and keep it going steady. Piecework. Fill the bucket, fill another, and still another. The competition was among a set of savages, as savage for money as himself, savages with machetes, hacking their way through the thickets of modern civilization back to the good old Aztec days, waiting to see who'd be first in line to wrench his heart out. Savage beasts, eager to fill as many buckets as possible in as short a time as possible, cleaning out an entire orchard, picking everything in sight clean, tons of fruit, delivering every bit of ripe fruit to the accountants in their cool air conditioned orifices.

The competition was not between pickers and growers.

It was between pickers—Jorge and Guillermo.

Between the poor and the hungry, the desperate, and the hunted, the slave and the slave, slob against slob, the depraved and himself. You were your own terrible boss. That was the cleverest part of the whole thing. The picker his own bone picker, his own willing built-in slave driver. God, that was good! That was where they reached into your scrotum and screwed you royally and drained your brain and directed your sinews and nerves and muscles with invisible fingers. To fatten their coffers. And drive you to your coffin. That sure was smart. Meant to be smart. Bookkeepers aren't dumb. You worked hard because you wanted to do that hard work above everything else. Pick fast pick hard pick furious pick pick pick. They didn't need straw bosses studying your neck to see if you kept bobbing up and down to keep your picking pace up. Like the barn-stupid chicken, you drove yourself to do it. You were your own money monkey foreman, monkey on top of your own back.

You over-charged yourself.

With your own frenzy.

Neat.

You pushed your gut and your tired aching arms and

your twitching legs pumping adrenalin until your tongue tasted like coarse sandpaper.

You didn't even stop to take a drink, let alone a piss, for fear you'd get fined, fired, or bawled out.

And then, after all that effort, you got your miserable pay.

Would the bobbing boss's sons stoop to that?

His fingers were loose and dexterous now. The plump orange balls plopped pitter patter like heavy drops of golden rain into his swaying, sweaty canvas bucket. His earnings depended entirely on how quickly he worked and how well he kept the pressure up. The morning sun was high. The sweet shade was fragrant and refreshing and comfortable under the leafy branches. The soil too was still cool and humid. It was going to be another hot one.

There.

Another row ended.

He swung around the end of the row and for a moment he was all alone, all by himself. He looked out far across the neighboring alfalfa field, dark green and rich and ripe. Then he looked at the long low Diablo Range close by, rising up into the misty pale blue air kept cool by the unseen bay nearby. This was all his. For a flowing, deceptive minute, all this rich, enormous terrain was all his. All this warm balmy baby air. All this healthful sunny breeze. All those hills, this rich fertile valley, these orchards, these tiled huertas, these magnificent farms all, all his . . . for his eyes to feast upon. It was a moment he wished he could capture forever and etch permanently on his memory, making it a part of living life for his heart to feast joyously on, forever. Why couldn't he stop? Why? Why couldn't he just put the bucket down and open his arms and walk into the hills and merge himself with the hills and just wander invisibly in the blue?

What Manuel couldn't really know was that he was completing yet another arc in the unending circle that had been started by one of his Mexican forebears exactly two hundred years before—for even the memory of history was also robbed from him—when Gaspar de Portola, hugging the coastline, nearing present-day San Francisco, climbed what is now Sweeney Ridge, and looked down upon San Francisco's magnificent landlocked Bay, overlooking what is now the International Airport.

Both don Gaspar and don Manuel were landlords and

landless at precisely the same instant of viewing all this heady beauty. And both were equally dispossessed. Both were also possessed of a keen sense of pride and natural absorption with the ritual and mystery of all life. The living that looked mighty good in a flash to Manuel lasted a good deal longer for don Gaspar whose stumbling accident swept him into honored and indelible pages of glorious history.

Manuel was now a mere straw among the enormous sludge of humanity flowing past, a creature of limb and his own driving appetites, a creature of heed and need. Swinging around another end run he placed his ladder on the next heavy limb of the next pregnant tree. He reached up. He plucked bunches of small golden fruit with both hands. He worked like a frenzied windmill in slow motion. He cleared away an arc as far as the circumference of his plucking fingers permitted. A living model for da Vinci's outstretched man. Adam heeding God's moving finger. He moved higher. He repeated another circle. Then down and around again to another side of the tree, until he cleared it, cleared it of all visible, viable, delectable, succulent fruit. It was sweet work. The biggest difference between him and the honey-gathering ant was that the ant had a home.

Several pickers were halfway down the next row, well in advance of him. He was satisfied he was pacing himself well. Most of the band was still behind him. The moving sun, vaulting the sky dome's crackling earth parting with its bronzing rays, pounded its fierce heat into every dead and living crevice. Perspiration poured down his sideburns, down his forehead, down his cheek, down his neck, into his ears, off his chin. He tasted its saltiness with the tip of his dry tongue. He wished he'd brought some salt tablets. Roberto Morales wasn't about to worry about the pickers, and Manuel wasn't worried either. Despite the heat, he felt some protection from the ocean and bay. It had been much, much worse in Texas, and much hotter in Delano in the San Joaquin valley and worst of all in Satan's own land, the Imperial Valley.

No matter which way he turned, he was trapped in an endless maze of apricot trees, as though forever, neat rows of them, neatly planted, row after row, just like the blackest bars on the jails of hell. There had to be an end. There had to be. There—trapped. There had to be a way out. Locked. There had to be a respite. Animal. The buckets and the crates kept piling up higher. Brute. He felt alone. Though

surrounded by other pickers. Beast. Though he was per-
spiring heavily, his shirt was powder dry. Savage. The hot
dry air sucking every drop of living moisture from his brute
body. Wreck. He stopped and walked to the farthest end of
the first row for some water, raised the dented dipper from
the brute tank, drank the holy water in great brute gulps so
he wouldn't have to savor its tastelessness, letting it spill
down his torn shirt to cool his exhausted body, to replenish
his brute cells and animals pores and stinking follicles and
pig gristle, a truly refined wreck of an animal, pleased to
meetcha. Predator.

   Lunch.

   Almost too exhausted to eat, he munched his cheese with
tortillas, smoked on ashes, then lay back on the cool ground
for half an hour. That short rest in the hot shade replen-
ished some of his humor and resolve. He felt his spirit swell
out again like a thirsty sponge in water. Then up again. The
trees. The branches again. The briarly branches. The
scratching leaves. The twigs tearing at his shirt sleeves. The
ladder. The rough bark. The endlessly unending piling up
of bucket upon box upon crate upon stack upon rack upon
mound upon mountain. He picked a mountain of cots automatically. An automator. A beast. A ray of enemy sun
penetrated the tree that was hiding him and split his forehead open. His mind whirred. He blacked out. Luckily he'd
been leaning against a heavy branch. His feet hooked to
the ladder's rung. His half-filled bucket slipped from his
grasp and fell in slow motion, splattering the fruit he'd so
laboriously picked. To the ground. Roberto happened by
and shook his head. "Whatsamatter, can't you see straight,
pendejo." Manuel was too tired even to curse. He should
have had some salt pills.

   Midafternoon.

   The summer's fierce zenith passed overhead. It passed.
Then dropped. It started to light the ocean behind him, back
of the hills. Sandy dreams. Cool nights. Cold drinks. Soft
guitar music with Lupe sitting beside him. All wafting
through his feverish moments. Tiredness drained his spirit
of will. Exhaustion drained his mind. His fingers burned.
His arms flailed the innocent trees. He was slowing down.
He could hardly fill his last bucket. Suddenly the whistle
blew. The day's work at last ended.

   Ended!

   The contratista Roberto Morales stood there.

His feet straddled. Mexican style. A real robber. A Mexican general. A gentlemanly, friendly, polite, grinning, vicious, thieving brute. The worst kind. To his own people. Despite his being a fellow Mexican, despite his torn old clothing, everyone knew what kind of clever criminal he was. Despite his crude, ignorant manner, showing that he was one of them, that he'd started with them, that he grew up with them, that he'd suffered all the sordid deprivations with them, he was actually the shrewdest, smartest, richest cannibal in forty counties around. They sure couldn't blame the gueros for this miscarriage. He was a crew chief. How could anyone know what he did to his own people? And what did the gueros care? So the anglo growers and guero executives, smiling in their cool filtered offices, puffing their elegant thin cigars, washed their clean blond bloodless dirtless hands of the whole matter. All they did was hire Roberto Morales. Firm, fair and square. For an agreed-upon price. Good. How he got his people down to the pickings was no concern of theirs. They were honest, those gueros. They could sleep at night. They fulfilled their end of the bargain, and cheated no one. Their only crime; their only soul grime indeed was that they just didn't give a shit how that migratory scum lived. It was no concern of theirs. Their religion said it was no concern of theirs. Their wives said it was no concern of theirs. Their aldermen said it was no concern of theirs. Their—

Whenever Roberto Morales spoke, Manuel had to force himself not to answer. He had to keep his temper from flaring.

"Now," announced Morales at last, in his friendliest tone. "Now, I must take two cents from every bucket. I am sorry. There was a miscalculation. Everybody understands. Everybody?" He slid his eyes around, smiling, palms up.

The tired, exhausted pickers gasped as one.

Yes. Everyone understood. Freezing in place. After all that hard work.

"Any questions, men?"

Still grinning, knowing, everyone realizing that he had the upper hand, that would mean a loss of two or three dollars out of each picker's pay that day, a huge windfall for Morales.

"You promised to take nothing!" Manuel heard himself saying. Everyone turned in astonishment to stare at Manuel.

"I said two cents hombre. You got a problem or what?"

"You promised."

The two men, centered in a huge ring of red-ringed eyes, glared at each other. Reaching for each other's jugular. The other exhausted animals studied the tableau through widening eyes. It was so unequal. Morales remained calm, confident, studying Manuel. As though memorizing his features. He had the whole advantage. Then, with his last remaining energy, Manuel lifted his foot and clumsily tipped over his own last bucket of cots. They rolled away in all directions around everyone's feet.

Roberto Morales' eyes blazed. His fists clenched. "You pick them up, Gutierrez."

So. He knew his name. After all. For answer, Manuel kicked over another bucket, and again the fruit rolled away in in all directions.

Then an astonishing thing happened.

All the other pickers moved toward their own buckets still standing beside them on the ground awaiting the truck gatherer, and took an ominous position over them, straddling their feet over them. Without looking around, without taking his eyes off Manuel, Roberto Morales said sharply, "All right. All right, men. I shall take nothing this time."

Manuel felt a thrill of power course through his nerves. He had never won anything before. He would have to pay for this, for his defiance, somehow, again, later. But he had shown defiance. He had salvaged his money savagely and he had earned respect from his fellow slaves. The gringo hijos de la chingada would never know of this little incident, and would probably be surprised, and perhaps even a little mortified, for a few minutes. But they wouldn't give a damn. It was bread, pan y tortillas out of his children's mouths. But they still wouldn't give a single damn. Manuel had wrenched Morales' greedy fingers away and removed a fat slug of a purse from his sticky grasp. And in his slow way, in his stupid, accidental, dangerous way, Manuel had made an extravagant discovery, as don Gaspar had also made two centuries before, in almost exactly the same spot. And that was—that a man counted for something. For men, Manuel dimly suspected, are built for something more important and less trifling than the mere gathering of prunes and apricots, hour upon hour, decade upon decade, insensibly, mechanically, antlike. Men are built to experience a certain sense of honor and pride.

Or else they are dead before they die.

II

Contemporary
Chicano Poetry

Introduction

At least to date, by far the most prolific writing by Chicano writers has been poetry. Many Spanish-language newspapers contain at least a poem or two, the journals of Mexican-American prisoner groups usually contain some poetry, and of course the Chicano monthlies and quarterlies are a good source of this form of Chicano art. Finally, outpourings of poetry and artwork are being published at several colleges and universities that have established Chicano studies programs. This outpouring of poetry by Chicano writers should not be surprising. The most popular literary form among Chicanos has long been the corrido, a ballad sung to the accompaniment of a guitar and often circulated in broadside, usually about an important event or popular hero. Zapata, Villa, Gregorio Cortez, and lately Cesar Chavez and Reies Tijerina have all been celebrated in numerous corridos.

There is no dominant formal "school" of Chicano poetry, and no consistent use of formal devices that would tend to identify one. In respect to its prosody, it is largely free verse, though often quite musical, and when rhymed, often marked by the Spanish, rather than the English, verse tradition. Perhaps the most obvious quality of Chicano verse is its spontaneity (although we suspect this is often a studied effect), freshness, and honesty. Much of the poetry contains lines in Spanish or a dialect of Spanish, reflecting the roots of a bilingual people who revert in times of stress to the more familiar tongue of the home. Footnotes will provide translations for those lines that are dominantly in Spanish, and the glossary will provide definitions of all Spanish words that are neither obvious cognates nor extremely obvious from the context, throughout the text.

The first poem, "Aztec Mother," by Leonardo Elias, celebrates the "brown Virgin," of Guadalupe, patron of the Mexican, in a most touching way. Elias is presently a prisoner in a federal penitentiary.

The next six poems, from *Floricanto,* by Alurista, reflect

a depth of knowledge about both the culture of *La Raza* and poetry as a literary art. Thematically, the poems deal with vital Chicano issues: "Chicano power," self-assertion, the barrio, the Virgin of Guadalupe, and the conflict between Chicano and *Yanqui* cultures. All of his poems seem permeated with that philosophy of hope common to Chicano literature, which we have mentioned above. Yet Alurista's poetry is not only topically significant, he is a master of tactile and visual imagery, and his English lines are sometimes rhymed in the Spanish pattern of assonance and consonance.

"A Delano," a poem by Jorge Gonzalez from *El Ombligo* (he is the technical editor of the book), treats, as its title claims, the grape strike at Delano, California. The *huelga* is seen by the poet, and by most Chicanos, as the symbolic moment when the Chicano cause coalesced. The poem is in essence a song for victory, a plea for the unification of body and spirit, the "guns and pens" of the poem, to produce one whole and triumphant expression.

"Mi Hombre" by Gloria Perez is a poem lauding the revolution and, as is obvious from the references, evocative of the revolution and at the same time, a love poem. In the coming battle for equality, the Chicana will stand and fight alongside her man, lending him mental, physical, and moral support, much in the manner of the brave Mexican women who accompanied the revolutionaries in victory, in flight, in defeat, and in final triumph.

"Tecatos" by Gallo Kirach is a young Chicano's inpressionistic view of the city and the cultural conflict between Chicanos and Anglos, here symbolized by the streetcorner conflict between several *vatos locos* drug users and the police. The poem is a scream of protest, yet at the same time a lament, reminiscent in style and content of Allen Ginsberg's "Howl."

"Católicos por La Raza" by Cesar Lopez concerns another central problem or issue in the Chicano experience, the Catholic Church, "the biggest chingazo . . ." which the poet accuses of being overly concerned with money and real estate and too little concerned with its people, a charge long familiar in Latin America and a central issue in the Mexican Revolution. Stylistically, the poem makes use of several *vato* dialect expressions. The final selection from *El Ombligo*, "No Se Puede Olvidar," by Manuel Gomez, is a passionate plea for Chicano unity.

"Aztec Angel" and "Robstown" are both from Omar Salinas's *Crazy Gypsy*, a volume of verse that does not limit itself to purely Chicano problems, but to universal human ones. Nevertheless, "Aztec Angel" is a kaleidoscopic study of Chicano identity. The speaker in the poem is an "Aztec angel/forlorn passenger/on a train/of chicken farmers/and happy children" who, searching for himself finds that he is the offspring/of a woman/who was beautiful." This is a clear appeal for Chicano pride, done up in the classic form of the journey of discovery. We find here that identity with the Indian, the Aztec, with *Aztlan,* that seems to dominate the tripartite identity of the Chicanos when one studies their poets. "Robstown," the second poem by Salinas, is a sketch of small-town Texas during the late forties, where "Anitas brother/has a Congressional/and they/wouldn't /serve him/at Texas/restaurant." The poem indicts also the passivity of the Chicana mother, who symbolizes all of the old, bad, ways of resignation and acceptance of second-class status when she says: "We'll go to/the rosary/at San Antonio/and pray." Salinas seems peculiarly adept at pruning and trimming the language in his poetry to its roots of truth, to essential statements of an existential reality.

The poems of Abelardo [Delgado] included in this anthology come from a remarkable collection, *CHICANO: 25 Pieces of a Chicano Mind*. It is unique that this collection, which tries "to depict the Chicano heart," is written in English, Spanish and the *Pocho** dialect. At times one poem uses both English and Spanish as in "El Chisme" or English alone in "Stupid America." This versatility of language is reflected also in the diverse themes of the poems. The old neighborhood gossip who "can penetrate solid steel (when she wants to) reach an ear," the Americanized son who joins the Boy Scouts, and the janitor who wishes to advance himself but fears an image as a sellout ("El Vendido") are treated with humorous, soft thrusts of satire. Stronger in its tone of ironic protest, "Stupid America" portrays the racist attitude of an America that views the Chicano as a criminal or at very least, trash. Finally, in "La Causa," Abelardo voices the triumph of the new consciousness of pride and awareness that allows ". . . the faceless chicanos

* *Pocho* is a term used by Mexican nationals to characterize a person of Mexican ancestry born in the United States. It is sometimes a derogatory term applied to brown people who ape Anglo ways. The *Pocho* dialect, or *pochismo*, is a mixture of Spanish and English, characterized by Spanish pronunciation of English words.

of that day to go/like eagles, as high as they can, as high as
they want to."

"Journey II" by raúlrsalinas shares in the epic theme of
so much of the Chicano literature we have discussed, as the
poet takes the reader on an autobiographical journey through
childhood and the loss of innocence in a Texas barrio. The
poem is cast in the confessional mode of Robert Lowell's
Life Studies, placing it well within the contemporary literary aesthetic.

The next poems are from Ricardo Sánchez's *Canto y
Grito Mi Liberación.* "Migrant Lament" is not in fact a lament at all, but rather a song for victory and pride. After
Delano, the stoop labor must stoop no more, at least meta-
phorically.

"It Is Urgent" is about the central theme of Chicano
identity, and insists that *La Raza* will not only endure,
but ultimately prevail. Sanchez's words seem to burn with
fervor and conviction, and the reader accepts his truth from
the very impact of his feeling.

Our final poetic selection, "El Peregrino" by Aristeo
Brito, Jr., is appropriate to cap the poetry selections in this
book. "El Peregrino" is almost a hymn to *Aztlan* and the
uniqueness of Chicano identity that could serve as the "We
shall overcome" of the Chicano revolution. Or, in Brito's
own words: "Aztlan is in the soul of our Chicanos!"

Aztec Mother

Leonardo Elias

Thank you beautiful bronze mother, for being yourself all this time. From the conquest of Mexico, to the present day, you are still the beautiful bronze afterglow in my heart.

You have suffered through wars and now you are suffering from discrimination and prejudice. I know my beautiful bronze mother, that you will persist to find a way to peace and happiness for your children. The road to freedom is rough; my heart hungers with the cries of love for all the Raza to come together as one.

With these last words I ask you beautiful Aztec mother, kiss my lips with death or touch my heart with peace. . . .

when raza?

Alurista

when raza?
when . . .
    yesterday's gone
and
    mañana
mañana doesn't come [1]
    for he who waits
no morrow
    only for he who is now
to whom when equals now
he will see a morrow
mañana la Raza

[1] tomorrow
  tomorrow doesn't come

> la gente que espera
> no verá mañana
> our tomorrow es hoy
>   ahorita
> que VIVA LA RAZA
>   mi gente [2]
> our people to freedom
>   when?
> now, ahorita define tu mañana hoy [3]

[2] tomorrow La Raza
the people who wait
will not see tomorrow
our tomorrow is today
right now
long live La Raza
my people
[3] now, right now define your tomorrow today

in the barrio sopla el viento

Alurista

> in the barrio sopla el viento [1]
>   the stench
>   of the cannery permeates
>   the air
> and mi gente breathes [2]
>   the secretions
>   of cancerous system
>   suicidal infection
> drags mi gente
>   a la siembra inmunda [3]
>   and to the frigid factory
> to spray on our open wounds
>   de yugo opresivo
>   esclavizante
> la pestilencia [4]

[1] in the barrio the wind blows
[2] and my people breathes
[3] drags my people
to the filthy field
[4] of oppressive yoke
enslaving
the pestilence

       of its diseased skeleton
and the dust
       our breath
sweeps
       and whistles
our alienated pride

must be the season of the witch

Alurista

       must be the season of the witch
              la bruja
              la llorona [1]
       she lost her children
              and she cries
       en las barrancas of industry [2]
              her children
       devoured by computers
       and the gears
       must be the season of the witch
              i hear huesos crack [3]
       in pain
              y lloros
       la bruja pangs
              sus hijos han olvidado
       la magia de durango
              y la de moctezuma
                     —el huiclamina [4]
       must be the season of the witch
       la bruja llora
       sus hijos sufren; sin ella [5]

[1] the witch
   the wailing one
[2] in the ravines of industry
[3] I hear bones crack
[4] and weeping
   witch pangs
   her children have forgotten
   the magic of Durango
   and that of Moctezuma
   the Huiclamina
[5] the witch cries
   her children suffer, without her

en el barrio

Alurista

en el barrio
—en las tardes de fuego [1]
when the dusk prowls
en la calle desierta
pues los jefes y jefas
trabajan [2]
—often late hours
after school
we play canicas [3]
in the playground
abandoned and dark
sin luces
hasta la noche
we play canicas [4]
until we grow
to make borlote [5]
and walk the streets
con luces [6]
paved—with buildings
altos como el fuego
—el que corre en mis venas [7]

[1] in the barrio
in the fiery afternoons
[2] in the deserted street
for the fathers and mothers
work
[3] we play marbles
[4] without lights
until night
. . . marbles
[5] to have a great time
[6] with lights
[7] high as the fire
that runs through my veins

fruto de bronce [1]

Alurista

i've seen
i've seen

[1] bronze fruit

i've seen the bronze child
    —on his little (round) head,
    hair locks of black
    rizados cabellos
y su madre
    —su madre
    su madre guadalupe
con el infante
en sus brazos [2]
i've seen her bronze skin
    guadalupe madre
vientre bendito
    y su fruto de bronce
ChicaNos
    los dos [3]
i've seen the bronze birth
    el nacimiento

    el nacimiento
el nacimiento de mi pueblo [4]
bronze child,
bronze skin,
bronze virgin,
        i have seen the bronze birth
    —la guadalupe de bronce
ha parido a mi pueblo
    al infante
    a los niños
    —a los batos
    a la plebe
    —a la gente

[2] curly hair
    —and his mother
    his mother Guadalupe
    with the infant
    in her arms
[3] mother Guadalupe
    blessed womb
    and its bronze fruit
    chicanos
    the two
[4] the birth
    the birth
    the birth of my people

                    a la Raza [5]
         i have seen
              i have seen
         i have seen la Raza
              i have seen la Raza
         i have seen la Raza be born

[5] the bronze Guadalupe
   has given birth to my people
   to the infant
   to the children
   to the dudes
   to the masses
   to the people
   to La Raza

can this really be the end?

Alurista

    can this really be the end
              out to hand a jump right in
    come see her, come on now
         to Chicano town go down
         again
    a-ver la feria de colores cuetes
              campanas
         y ventanas de cartón
    paredes de papel, terruño seco pizo
    al bautizo de san juan [1]
    dove descending drifting dead on head
    of christos, the man jesús
         he ain't dead
    pedro will tell you in a rezo [2] to the sun
    y macario su rosario y su misal [3]
    dog chow cookies? belly lead?
    to shoot? to kill?
         and crumble melting in a wall,

[1] to see the fair, firecrackers
   and cardboard windows
   dry plot of land
   to the baptism of San Juan
[2] prayer
[3] his rosary and missal

blood spilt?
　　　　paredes tatuadas,
　pardon final,
　　　muerto? ¡chale! [4]
we're alive Raza!

[4] tattooed walls
final pardon
dead? No!

a delano

Jorge Gonzalez

a delano,[1]
caravanas de comida,[2]
de san diego y oakland.
hunger to satiate
of illegal origins.
bodies work
minds think
but, together they don't caravan.
so we hunger.
raza bronze [3]
cuerpo y mente [4]
guns and pens
juntos venceremos.[5]

[1] to Delano
[2] caravans of food
[3] bronze race
[4] body and mind
[5] together we will win.

mi hombre[1]

Gloria Perez

like the sumptuous
pyramids of tenochtitlán,
mi hombre
you stand in my mind
y en mi corazón,[2]
erect,
like the bronze statue
of a man,

[1] my man
[2] and in my heart

mi hombre,
         being bathed
by the never ending
         flames of ometeotl,
como la adelita [3]
         siempre al lado
del guerrillero,[4]
         i'll live with you,
i'll hunger with you,
         i'll bleed with you,
and i'll die with you.

[3] like the *adelita*
[4] always at the side
   of the guerilla

tecatos[1]

Gallo Kirach

midnight streets
paved with human souls of bronze
sentenced to street corner cantinas [2]
for ever
         journeys
to prison hell
indian eyes glaring at barrio [3] sisters
         aztlán [4] oaths taken
in the womb of our mother machismo [5]
morritas [6] shake hips
and money hungry doctors water
         at the mouth of white coat garbage cans.
humanity's welfare state of
         equality
and
         compassion.

[1] drug users, addicts, heroin users
[2] saloons, bars, taverns
[3] the section of town peopled by Chicanos:
   often segregated, often a slum
[4] the Aztec nation today, an abstract
   concept of a great nation
   peopled by Mexican-Americans
[5] manliness
[6] girls (slang)

mariachi bands [7] singing their corazones [8] hoarse
while police sirens in neon jungles write
on the silent blackboard of problems
    never solved.
ibm machines and plastic people
running in forest of rain
    conventions in chicago.
handcuffs and police helmets stalking carga
senile judgements of pedos [9] suffocated.
judas priest wearing gerard shoes.
dominos playing in prison yards
of street corner jets soaring by
    skeletons
and vatos locos [10] dying like men.

[7] the traditional Mexican band
[8] heart
   testicles
[9] literally "farts"
[10] crazy guys: the young and desperate
   youth of the barrio

Católicos por La Raza[1]

Cesar Lopez

"la dignidad del hombre
    es la paz" dijo villa
mas pienso,[2]
when we are born
    we pay for birth
when holy communion comes around
    we pay
get married
    we pay and,
finally,
    the biggest chingazo comes. . . .[3]
we have to pay for dying;
    i want to die free.
ya ni la chigan, carnal [4]

[1] Catholics for La Raza
[2] "the dignity of man
is peace" said villa
but I think
[3] the biggest rip-off comes
[4] and now the final rip-off, brother

at least once
i want to be free of payment;
    when i die.
la ley del hombre is not [5]
    without payment
all i can pay is my faith
and i believe
    my death to be my freedom
let me rest in peace
    where my dignity rests.

[5] the law of man is not

no se puede olvidar[1]

Manuel Gomez

simon carnales,[2]
    we have all traveled
    a long dusty road
from probably painful births
    to the hot fields of colorado
    growing up pobre pero invencible,[3]
    to the hardened barrios of califas
    of unknown drunken stupors,
    to the shit of white schools,
        that suffocated our self-confidence
        with words that poisoned our souls,
to the juvies, jails, and prisons of
    the gabacho,[4] burning our
    mind with time,
to the painful pang of departure,
to the inevitable death drug ritual
    only to return to the painful present.
to the bitterness of our sweet
    moments
to the fast-fleeting memories
    of our pasts.
to this sick society

[1] one cannot forget
[2] all right, brothers
[3] growing up poor but invincible
[4] white man or Anglo

to shattered spiritual dreams
        all because of
            broken
                brotherhood_____

Aztec Angel

Omar Salinas

I

I am an Aztec angel
    criminal
        of a scholarly
            society
        I do favors
            for whimsical
                magicians
        where I pawn
            my heart
                for truth
            and find
                my way
        through obscure
                streets
            of soft spoken
                hara-kiris

II

I am the Aztec angel
    forlorn passenger
        on a train
    of chicken farmers
        and happy children

III

I am the Aztec angel
    fraternal partner
        of an orthodox
            society

where pachuco children
    hurl stones
through poetry rooms
and end up in a cop car
    their bones itching
        and their hearts
    busted from malnutrition

    IV

I am the Aztec angel
        who frequents bars
spends evenings
        with literary circles
    and socializes
        with spiks
niggers and wops
        and collapses on his way
            to funerals

    V

Drunk
    lonely
        bespectacled
    the sky
            opens my veins
              like rain
                clouds go berserk
              around me
            my Mexican ancestors
              chew my fingernails
I am an Aztec angel
    offspring
    of a woman
        who was beautiful

Robstown

Omar Salinas

    La llorona [1]
    is in town
    by the river

[1] Weeping woman, the weeping witch of Mexican folk tradition.

or so the people
say.

Tomorrow
the sun
of Robstown
will rise
at 6:15

and if we catch any
of you drunk Mexicans
on the street
we'll drive you
out of Town.

1947.

Mother why do they look
at us like
that?

We'll go to
the rosary
at San Antonio
and pray.

Anitas brother
has a Congressional
and they
wouldn't
serve him
at Texas
restaurant.

We'll go to
the rosary
at San Antonio
and pray.

San Antonio
        is the Catholic
                church in Robstown

Stupid America

Abelardo

stupid america, see that chicano
with a big knife

in his steady hand
he doesn't want to knife you
he wants to sit on a bench
and carve christfigures
but you won't let him.
stupid america, hear that chicano
shouting curses on the street
he is a poet
without paper and pencil
and since he cannot write
he will explode.
stupid america, remember that chicanito
flunking math and english
he is the picasso
of your western states
but he will die
with one thousand masterpieces
hanging only from his mind.

El Vendido

Abelardo

my son is a sell out
he just became a boy scout.
I would like to entertain
the notion of sell outs
or vendidos as we say
a la chicano.
josé lopez has been working
as a janitor for the last twelve years
today he got a two dollar raise
and today also he has been accused
by the barrio of being a vendido,
josé is thinking very seriously
of refusing the raise
to preserve his barrio image.
if a man is not made
to deviate from his goal
all his actions,
whatever they may be,
disqualify him as a sell out.
a man sells out

the minute he compromises
with a different goal
and needs not the criticism
of his chicano brothers
for he (the funny thing about selling out)
pays for himself.
finally no chicano can sell himself
for you see, he is too dumb,
he has not arrived at a price
or could it be he is too wise.

La Causa
Abelardo

what moves you, chicano to stop being polite?
nice chicano could be patted on the head and wouldn't bite
and now, how dare you tell your boss, "go fly a kite"?
    es la causa, hermano, which has made me a new man.

what is this causa which disturbs your steady hand,
could it be an inherited love of land
or the indian impudence called pride that I can't
    understand?
    this causa, hermano, is charcoaled abuse ready to burn.

what nonsense this brown power that you claim,
what stupid demands erupt from wills untamed,
what of your poetic submissiveness that brought you fame?
    es la causa, hermano, which leaves no one untouched.

delano awaits the verdict of the nation,
del río and justice dance in wild anticipation,
el paso and *la causa* will be good for the duration
    es la causa, hermano, raping apathy with flair.

san antonio cannot sleep another night,
los angeles cannot forfeit another fight,
denver cannot hide from us its burning light,
    es la causa, hermano, don't let our heroes feel betrayed.

albuquerque trembles with the blast of sacrifice
y todo el valle carries life at a cheap price,[1]
los barrios y los campos become a symphony of cries,
    es la causa de la raza an anthill upon your chest.[2]

[1] and the whole valley
[2] the barrios and the fields

la causa for all those blindly involved who do not know
is the planting of mañanas which will grow
permitting the faceless chicanos of that day to go
  like eagles, as high as they can, as high as they want to.

El Chisme[1]

Abelardo

with more accuracy than ol' time pistolero [2]
and with the advantage of arriving there primero [3]
el chisme soap suds clean, the chicano's noticiero [4]
can penetrate solid steel con mas ganas [5] reach an ear.

la vecina's [6] zippered lip can, gentle, non offensive, appear
but even chet and david lack the details that she has
if she didn't see it happen se imagina lo que es,[7]
she's not happy with the facts till she turns them al revez.[8]

the network is so well organized that it now predicts
with much precision where the gallup polls will not come
    near
what the chisme gets going not the devil contradicts
and church canons look puny against the chisme's edicts.

what baffles even the most of modern computations
is how one chisme ruins a million reputations
and another broadcasting from the same mouth makes you
    dear
just proof that many tongues need immediate amputations.

[1] the gossip
[2] outlaw, gangster, gunman
[3] first
[4] news
[5] when it (he) wants to
[6] the neighbor
[7] she imagines what it is.
[8] wrong side out.

Journey II

raúlrsalinas

for my son Ricardo

They're tearing down the old school
    wherein i studied as a child
        Our Lady of Guadalupe . . .

Parochial prison/Internment camp for
      underprivileged Mexican kids,
          soon to be pummelled by
merciless wrecking ball.
      What do i remember best?
         What childhood mem'ries
cling stubbornly to the brain
      like bubble-gum under a table?

         Saturday afternoon Confession:
(it was no sweat giving up the li'l tadpole sins,
      spittin' out the big bullfrogs was the hassle.)
         unlit & cramped confessional closet
with only shadowy profile of Padre Jose,
      ever ready to impose heavy
         Our Father/Hail Mary sentence.
Catechism: Doctrina classes after school
    First Holy Communion Day!
        (i ingest
one of many sacraments to come
      & speak to the galaxies)
      white suit/*padrino* Chris/a ride in
         Posey's pre-war '38 Buick
The twins: Boffo & me fantasize,
      grown up—slaying dragons—planting corn
        if they would marry us.
Climbing, zooming heavenward, up rickety
      stairs into chamber of horrors/haunted
        house of learning . . . viewed by un-
suspecting boyzngirlz as transylvanian
      castle of doom.
       "No, 'Minga, those weren't black
ghosts flying around on lofty 5th. floor
      balustrade, just Sisters' penguin-like
      habits; hanging out to dry."
The unforgettable recital: tribute to John Philip
      Sousa, in abandoned subterranean lunchroom.
        All dress'd up like cadets. i played the
triangle. Big deal! The seamstress goofed on
      my uniform. Each time triangle went . . . ting!
       . . . oversized trousers slipped down
another inch. Trusty blue/gray lunchbox:
      opened many a coin-slot
        on schoolyard bullies' heads.

Singing "God Bless America": would you believe?
    Competing for the lead with my friend Fernando . . .
The one who, like Nash & cousin Albino, never
      returned that Saturday; from gathering palms
        for Palm Sunday . . . crushed beneath grinding
locomotive wheels.
    How unreal it all seems now.
      They MUST have gone to heaven;
how could any God deny them entrance?
    Such beautiful people . . . young plants
      who never lived to blossom.
With their deaths life lost all meaning.
    Fernando: my competitor in song—Albino: cohort
      in chasing girls—Nash: (good ol' thoughtful
      Nash)
never once forgot my birthday.
    How unfair . . . unkindly
      they were stripped from my being.
"if only good people go to heaven when they die,
    i done blew my chance of ever seeing them again."

      Strutting birdbreast stuck way out, smoking
WINGS cigarettes. Great big eyes for Juanita what's-
    her-name. Treating demure Catholic young ladies
      to unpaid-for Kress's 5 & 10¢ birthstone rings
inducing them to smoke . . . too soon busted!
    Reprimanded.
    Forced to kneel prostrate before giant crucifix and
      Sister Hermaneda. Tender knuckles kissed by
wooden ruler. Sorry, wrong rhumba.
    Carlin's Place: our crowd o' rowdies jitterbugging
      me watching.
"You got to ac-cen-tuate the positive, e-li-mi-nate the
    negative, don' mess with Mr. in-between."
      Sounds: Mercer, Woody & The Duke
"Couldn't make it without you, don't get around
    much anymore."

    A thousand merry harlequins dance happily/
nostalgically inside my head.
    The families whose sons n' daughters
      became priests & nuns.

i wonder what percentage of us
    turned nomadic children
        of the streets?
AGNES MARIE: because you were who you were,
    i'd name a daughter after you. i still possess the
        comic valentine you sent me. The one of a
gawky/gangly gal in bathing suit & water-wings, which
read: "Lissen punk, you be mine or i'm sunk!"
    So many times i've seen you, as i turned a corner/
        crossed a street, in so many different cities. But—
unlike Dante—the you i saw was never really you.

        The 1st. hip priest encountered—Father Busch—
Father Green was also pretty much aware;
    in that long ago, before the era of NOW clergymen:
        BRIGANTI & GOERTZ.
"Polished Pebbles": worn-out operetta
    year-in-year-out performance by seniors
        at uptight Knights of Columbus Hall.
To this day i've yet to know
    who penned that lame libretto of corn!

        The sandpile in back of Joseph's Garage
the little pasture at the French Legation:
    first experiments with sex conducted there.
        Josie luring us to Confederate cemetery for
advanced lessons. i chicken out and run. So,
    wherever you may be J., i apologize.
        i just wasn't ready.

Sister Armela:
    i've got news for you;
        Ivory Soap Don't Taste Worth A Damn!
And all i ever said was *DAMN!!!*
    The busted water fountain which i didn't bust.
        Ask God, He'll tell you i didn't do it.
Snitchin' Teresa said i did.

    E-X-P-U-L-S-I-O-N!

        Retaliation/paintbrush in hand/no longer
dull abandoned lunchroom. Red paint on sickly-green walls.
    Me an' my rappie—Joe Giddy—decorate the dingy
        cellar and defy the Gods.

"CATCH ME IF YOU CAN, YOU'LL NEVER TAKE
    ME

ALIVE."—signed MR. X . . . "GOD IS DEAD AND
     BURIED
IN THIS DINER THAT NEVER FED ANYONE." "THE
EASTSIDE TERRORS STRIKE AGAIN."
          Yeah, i did it,
        you shoulda' never kicked me out, father.
i loved the school in my own way.
Even if it was mostly prayers, i still learned something.
        There's still a couple of guys
            i'm pretty tight with/communicate with: like
Ol' St. Jude Thaddeus, who's had Miz' Hill
        on her knees these 36 years;
          & St. Dismas, he's one of the fellows.
He *knew* what was happening!

There's more . . . much more . . . an infinite voyage
        on a route paved with invaluable gems
          to treasure forever.
When i was out last time, i visited the old school
        once again. It had changed some. A section of
            the old spook house facade was gone, a modern
cracker-box was in its place. i would have lingered
        to catch a few vibrations of that other world, but
          i was a sick poet that day. My only concern
was the 4 caps of medicine someone had left under
        a rock for me. i thought of going back the next day.

        A prior commitment with the courts of law
made this impossible.
        i won't be there for the razing,
            but i'll return when i'm an aged, wizened man.
When freedom doves are on the wing again,
        i must go back and savor long the taste
            of spirits from another era (long before
the fall of innocence), upon my famished heart.

        And if there is a parking lot
            erected on that sacred spot

                i'll blow it up with dynamite

        and think of everything
            it meant to me . . .

migrant lament . . .

Ricardo Sánchez

el cri-cri llanudo [1]

canto y desmadre [2]
among migrant deprivation;
schools filled
with tejanitos [3]
fighting carnales [4]
in ethnocentric heresy . . .

gringo asking
'bout right kind of chicanos—
people leaders
succumbing to right answers . . .

migrant
tumbling offtowork,
saca llena de algodón,[5]
from tejas to colorado,
michigan to oregón . . .

la raza hurt,
bent back—sacrified
to gringoismo—
priests genuflecting
to pobreza.[6]
lovers of destitution;

priests jiving la raza,
preaching
  LOVE THY MASTER
   OF THE BLUE-EYED HATRED;
a new age
has dawned,

[1] the lonely cricket chirps
[2] motherless (luckless, hopeless)
[3] with Texans
[4] fighting brothers
[5] sack full of cotton
[6] to poverty

            you, migrant hecho del duelo,[7]
            scurry thru your work,
from lettuce strike
to grape boycott,
you laugh with new machismo.

migrant,
weep not over past desmadres
pick up coraje y cojones [8]
and
create
        una
           ôbra social
               mundial [9] . . .

[7] made of sorrow
[8] pick up courage and manliness
[9] a
  social work
  worldwide

it is urgent

Ricardo Sánchez

   it is urgent
to re-cant
the question
of our human-ness;

it is basic
to our nature
to foliate our sense of being;

life/force surging out
poetically blazing out
our societal-viewpoint activism;

knowing, feeling, being
human universality
cauterizing canto y llanto,[1]
fortalizing humanity,

creating sensitivity
while charting
human courses . . .

[1] song and cry

WHO ARE WE?
we are the urgent voices
venting expletives

praising our haunted sense
stemming from our human-ness . . .

WE ARE UNIVERSAL MAN,
a spectral rivulet,
multi-hued and beautiful—

WE ARE LA RAZA [2]

the cradle of civilization
crucible of human-ness
yesterday, today, & tomorrow

MESTIZO [3] HUMAN-NESS.

[2] the race, the Mexican people
[3] a person of mixed (usually Spanish and Indian) ancestry

El Peregrino

Aristeo Brito, Jr.

Aztlan, the promised land of the Chicano.
Immense reservoir for the rain of stars.
Fire and sun! Emerald fields, azure sky,
Aztlan is the horizon of crystalline magic
Which mates the earth to heaven.
How enchanting is heaven's burning passion!
How the clouds glow with its heat!
How cold the moon!
Aztlan is the alpha of the four winds, where heaven and
    earth are one,
Its god is the sun marching westward on blue peaks,
Its beauty is crimson by the cold silver of the moon.
Through a mirage of crystal,
Through its beautiful reflections
The chicano marches on

He runs enchanted toward pure waters,
And from the well he takes the darkness of the night.
Slowly moving through a trackless path,
The boy turns the mist red
With his sacrificing feet
Without the cricket's song, without the owl's lantern,
The mountain path is lost in among the green
The icy waters of the moon feed the pilgrim
And he trembles.
—Mother, my feet bleed, but they don't hurt,
The moon cuts, but I don't feel.
My cry rents the air, but I don't hear . . .
Oh! the road is lost in the night!
—Sleep my child, and rest
Heaven will take care that you always have the best . . .
And the boy returns to sleep to the smile of the moon
Soon the cook crows and the city lady hides.
Aztlan returns at dawn to a baptism of dew.
Bring a serenade of birds for the child who awakes.
Lovely flowers give new life to the Chicano's land.
Yet . . .
—Mother, I could not sleep, a woman followed me . . .
—Sleep my child and rest . . .
—Mommy, my hands are cold, my body is chilled . . .
—Heaven will take care that you always have the best . . .
Mami, I raise my eyes to heaven, but they are heavy on my
    soul . . .
O'er fields, o'er the land, in the wind
Sadness is foretold.
The sky's in smoke, gunpowder, and rifles,
Terror is grey in the pelt of dogs,
Shattered are the windows of the soul.
To the stench of incense, of factory, of death,
The fields answer with a black hue,
A hue that twists the vines in pain,
Hats explode through the fists of man,
And in the desert, the sahuaro,
The sentinel who drinks the pungent wine of tears;
In the other arid lands
There are strokes of mea culpa in the depths of oil wells,
Hammer blows on the bones of the dead . . .
Slow the steps, funeral march, a song for the pilgrim.
Peace, Silence the boy bites his cry.
Aztlan is lost in a haze.

No mother! Aztlan is not lost! It affirms itself in us.
Aztlan is the bosom that feels, that cries, that fights and
    dreams.
It's earth and heaven with stretching hands to our brothers,
Aztlan is in the soul of our Chicanos!

III

Contemporary
Chicano Drama

Introduction

Insofar as we are able to determine, there are no conventional dramatic works in print by Chicano authors, and we are certain that there are none informed by the thematic basis we have chosen to use in this volume. Yet there is a viable and extremely important Chicano theater, the *Teatro Campesino* of Luis Valdez. The *Teatro* is, we feel, so original and important a contribution to our national literature that we have included Valdez's own criticism about it, together with two of the *actos*. Yet some general remarks are in order. First of all, not only is the *Teatro* a genuine and wholly original art form produced by Chicanos, it is also quite importantly a genre that is designed almost exclusively for Chicanos, making it the only genre we have included that is purposefully conceived and acted by its own audience. As drama, the *Teatro* is an eclectic collection of several types of theater: the masque, the mime, the medieval morality play, the Mexican Ballet Folklorico, the Socialist agit-prop theater of the thirties, and finally, the street theater of the Black Arts Movement. Frankly propagandistic in nature, the *Teatro* was born of the picket lines at Delano, and uses broad humor, stereotyped characters, and even slapstick. Thankfully, unlike the Chinese "people's theater," the *Teatro* goes to great lengths to entertain as well as inform its audience, thereby meeting the basic criterion for literature, although it is hardly aesthetically pure. Moreover, although these written scripts obviously exist, more often than not its amateur actors ad-lib their parts, and departures from the script toward a more immediate relevance are encouraged.

Lorca dreamed of establishing a "people's" theater in pre-Civil war Spain, but never succeeded, possibly because his aesthetic sensibility was too fine for his audience, but Valdez, with the *Teatro Campesino* performing on picket lines, in hiring halls, church basements, village squares, and now in colleges and universities throughout the country has succeeded in making a people's theater a reality.

"Los Vendidos," the first of the two *actos* we have included is an attack on stereotyping, with "Honest Sancho's Used Mexican Lot" engaged in the business of peddling stereotypical Chicanos to the Anglo community for window dressing. An attack on white liberals and *vendidos* such as Miss Jimenez (she pronounces it Gym-in-ez as an ignorant Anglo would), the play is devastatingly funny, though, ironically, quite realistic.

"No Saco Nada de la Escuela" traces the academic careers of several Chicano students and their classmates from grade school through college and into the working world, while noting ironically that even the Black revolutionary is afforded better treatment than the Chicanos. Attacking both the racist school system and American society at large, there is little humor here except for derision.

It is hoped by the editors that these selections, representative of the best in contemporary Chicano literature, will expose the reader to an hitherto almost unknown body of work by a large, but to a great extent, tragically invisible, ethnic group in America. We hope also that the reader will be stimulated to further explore this rich lode of literature and culture through the reading of the original works and, finally, that he will become aware of the beauty and immediacy of Chicano art, and the tragic loss that can be suffered when a society denies cultural pluralism to pursue a chimera called "the American Dream."

The Actos

Luis Valdez

Nothing represents the work of "El Teatro Campesino" (and other teatros Chicanos) better than the *acto*. In a sense, the acto *is* Chicano theater, though we are now moving into a new, more mystical dramatic form we have begun to call the *mito*. The two forms are, in fact, cuates that complement and balance each other as day goes into night, el sol la sombra, la vida la muerte, el pajaro la serpiente. Our rejection of white western European (gavacho) proscenium theater makes the birth of new Chicano forms necessary—thus, los actos y los mitos; one through the eyes of man; the other, through the eyes of God.

The actos were born quite matter of factly in Delano. Nacieron hambrientos de la realidad. Anything and everything that pertained to the daily life, la vida cotidiana, of the huelguistas became food for thought, material for actos. The reality of campesinos on strike had become dramatic (and theatrical as reflected by newspapers, TV newscasts, films, etc.) and so the actos merely reflected the reality. Huelguistas portrayed Huelguistas, drawing their improvised dialogue from real words they exchanged with the esquiroles (scabs) in the fields everyday.

"Hermanos, compañeros, sálganse de esos files."
"Tenemos comida y trabajo para Uds. afuera de la Huelga."
"Esquirol, ten verguenza."
"Unidos venceremos."
"Sal de ah verigon!"

The first huelguista to portray an esquirol in the teatro did it to settle a score with a particularly stubborn scab he had talked with in the fields that day. Satire became a weapon that was soon aimed at known and despised contractors, growers, and mayordomos. The effect of those early actos on the huelguistas de Delano packed into

Filipino Hall was immediate, intense, and cathartic. The actos rang true to the reality of the Huelga.

Looking back at those early, crude, vital, beautiful, powerful actos of 1965, certain things have now become clear about the dramatic form we were just beginning to develop. There was, of course, no conscious deliberate plan to develop the *acto* as such. Even the name we gave our small presentations reflects the hard pressing expediency under which we worked from day to day. We could have called them "skits," but we lived and talked in San Joaquin Valley Spanish (with a strong Tejano influence), so we needed a name that made sense to the Raza. Cuadros, pasquines, autos, entremeses all seemed too highly intellectualized. We began to call them actos for lack of a better word, lack of time and lack of interest in trying to sound like classical Spanish scholars. De todos modos éramos Raza, quién se iba fijar?

The acto, however, developed its own structure through five years of experimentation. It evolved into a short dramatic form now used primarily by Los Teatros de Aztlan, but utilized to some extent by other non-Chicano guerilla theater companies throughout the U.S. including the San Francisco Mime Troupe and the Bread and Puppet Theater. (Considerable creative crossfeeding has occurred on other levels, I might add, between the Mime Troupe, the Bread and Puppet, and the Campesino.) Each of these groups may have their own definition of the acto, but the following are some of the guidelines we have established for ourselves over the years:

ACTOS: Inspire the audience to social action. Illuminate specific points about social problems. Satirize the opposition. Show or hint at a solution. Express what people are feeling.

So what's new, right? Plays have been doing that for thousand of years. True, except that the major emphasis in the acto is the social vision, as opposed to the individual artist or playwright's vision. Actos are not written; they are created collectively, through improvisation by a group. The reality reflected in an acto is thus a social reality, whether it pertains to campesinos or to vatos locos, not psychologically deranged self-projections but rather, group archetypes. Don Sotaco, Don Coyote, Johnny Pachuco, Juan Raza, Jorge el Chingon, la Chicana, are all group archetypes that have appeared in actos.

The usefulness of the acto extended well beyond the huelga into the Chicano movement, because Chicanos in general want to identify themselves as a group. The teatro archetypes symbolize the desired unity and group identity through Chicano heroes and heroines. One character can thus represent the entire Raza, and the Chicano audience will gladly respond to his triumphs or defeats. What to a non-Chicano audience may seem like oversimplification in an acto, is to the Chicano a true expression of his social state and therefore reality.

Los Vendidos[1]

Luis Valdez

1967

CHARACTERS: Honest Sancho
Miss Jimenez
Farm Worker
Pachuco
Revolucionario
Mexican-American

FIRST PERFORMANCE: Brown Beret junta, Elysian Park, East Los Angeles.

SCENE: Honest Sancho's Used Mexican Lot and Mexican Curio Shop. Three models are on display in Honest Sancho's shop: to the right, there is a revolucionario, complete with sombrero, carrilleras,[2] and carabina 30–30. At center, on the floor, there is the Farm Worker, under a broad straw sombrero. At stage left is the Pachuco, filero [3] in hand. *Honest Sancho is ʌoving among his models, dusting them off and preparing for another day of business.*

SANCHO: Bueno, bueno, mis monos, vamos a ver a quien vendemos ahora, no? (*To Audience*) Quihubo! [4] I'm Honest Sancho and this is my shop. Antes fui contratista pero ahora logre tener mi negocito.[5] All I need now is a customer. (*A bell rings offstage*) Ay, a customer!

SECRETARY: (*Entering*) Good morning, I'm Miss Jimenez from—

SANCHO: Ah, una chicana! Welcome, welcome Señorita Jimenez.

---

[1] sellouts
[2] literally chin straps, but may refer to cartridge belts
[3] blade
[4] "Good, good, my cute ones, let's see who we can sell now, O.K?"
[5] "I used to be a contractor, but now I've suceeded in having my little business."

[210]

SECRETARY: (*Anglo Pronunciation*) JIM-enez.

SANCHO: Qué?

SECRETARY: My name is Miss JIM-enez. Don't you speak English? What's wrong with you?

SANCHO: Oh, nothing, Señorita JIM-enez. I'm here to help you.

SECRETARY: That's better. As I was starting to say, I'm a secretary from Governor Reagan's office, and we're looking for a Mexican type for the administration.

SANCHO: Well, you come to the right place, lady. This is Honest Sancho's Used Mexican lot, and we got all types here. Any particular type you want?

SECRETARY: Yes, we were looking for somebody suave—

SANCHO: Suave.

SECRETARY: Debonair.

SANCHO: De buen aire.

SECRETARY: Dark.

SANCHO: Prieto.

SECRETARY: But of course not too dark.

SANCHO: No muy prieto.

SECRETARY: Perhaps, beige.

SANCHO: Beige, just the tone. Asi como cafecito con leche,[6] no?

SECRETARY: One more thing. He must be hardworking.

SANCHO: That could only be one model. Step right over here to the center of the shop, lady. (*They cross to the Farm Worker*) This is our standard farm worker model. As you can see, in the words of our beloved Senator George Murphy, he is "built close to the ground." Also take special notice of his 4-ply Goodyear huaraches, made from the rain tire. This wide-brimmed sombrero is an extra added feature—keeps off the sun, rain, and dust.

SECRETARY: Yes, it does look durable.

SANCHO: And our farm worker model is friendly. Muy amable.[7] Watch. (*Snaps his fingers*)

FARM WORKER: (*Lifts up head*) Buenos dias, señorita. (*His head drops*)

SECRETARY: My, he's friendly.

SANCHO: Didn't I tell you? Loves his patrones! But his most attractive feature is that he's hardworking. Let me show you. (*Snaps fingers. Farm Worker stands*)

[6] like coffee with milk
[7] very friendly

FARM WORKER: El jale! [8] (*He begins to work*)

SANCHO: As you can see he is cutting grapes.

SECRETARY: Oh, I wouldn't know.

SANCHO: He also picks cotton. (*Snap. Farm Worker begins to pick cotton*)

SECRETARY: Versatile, isn't he?

SANCHO: He also picks melons. (*Snap. Farm Worker picks melons*) That's his slow speed for late in the season. Here's his fast speed. (*Snap. Farm Worker picks faster*)

SECRETARY: Chihuahua . . . I mean, goodness, he sure is a hard worker.

SANCHO: (*Pulls the Farm Worker to his feet*) And that isn't the half of it. Do you see these little holes on his arms that appear to be pores? During those hot sluggish days in the field when the vines or the branches get so entangled, it's almost impossible to move, these holes emit a certain grease that allow our model to slip and slide right through the crop with no trouble at all.

SECRETARY: Wonderful. But is he economical?

SANCHO: Economical? Señorita, you are looking at the Volkswagen of Mexicans. Pennies a day is all it takes. One plate of beans and tortillas will keep him going all day. That, and chile. Plenty of chile. Chile jalapeños, chile verde, chile colorado. But, of course, if you do give him chile (*Snap. Farm worker turns left face. Snap. Farm worker bends over*), then you have to change his oil filter once a week.

SECRETARY: What about storage?

SANCHO: No problem. You know these new farm labor camps our Honorable Governor Reagan has built out by Parlier or Raisin City? They were designed with our model in mind. Five, six, seven, even ten in one of those shacks will give you no trouble at all. You can also put him in old barns, old cars, riverbanks. You can even leave him out in the field overnight with no worry!

SECRETARY: Remarkable.

SANCHO: And here's an added feature: every year at the end of the season, this model goes back to Mexico and doesn't return, automatically, until next spring.

SECRETARY: How about that. But tell me, does he speak English?

SANCHO: Another outstanding feature is that last year this

[8] the job

model was programmed to go out on STRIKE! (*Snap*)

FARM WORKER: HUELGA! HUELGA! Hermanos, sálganse de esos files.[9] (*Snap. He stops*)

SECRETARY: No! Oh no, we can't strike in the State Capitol.

SANCHO: Well, he also scabs. (*Snap*)

FARM WORKER: Me vendo barato, y qué? (*Snap*)

SECRETARY: That's much better, but you didn't answer my question. Does he speak English?

SANCHO: Bueno . . . no, pero [10] he has other—

SECRETARY: No.

SANCHO: Other features.

SECRETARY: No! He just won't do!

SANCHO: Okay, okay pues. We have other models.

SECRETARY: I hope so. What we need is something a little more sophisticated.

SANCHO: Sophisti—que?

SECRETARY: An urban model.

SANCHO: Ah, from the city! Step right back. Over here in this corner of the shop is exactly what you're looking for. Introducing our new 1969 Johnny Pachuco model! This is our fast-back model. Streamlined. Built for speed, low-riding, city life. Take a look at some of these features. Mag shoes, dual exhausts, green chartreuse paint-job, dark-tint windshield, a little poof on top. Let me just turn him on. (*Snap, Johnny walks to stage center with a pachuco bounce*)

SECRETARY: What was that?

SANCHO: That, señorita, was the Chicano shuffle.

SECRETARY: Okay, what does he do?

SANCHO: Anything and everything necessary for city life. For instance, survival: he knife fights. (*Snap. Johnny pulls out switchblade and swings at Secretary. Secretary screams*)

SANCHO: He dances. (*Snap*)

JOHNNY: (*Singing*) "Angel Baby, my Angel Baby . . ." (*Snap*)

SANCHO: And here's a feature no city model can be without. He gets arrested, but not without resisting, of course. (*Snap*)

JOHNNY: En la madre, la placa.[11] I didn't do it! I didn't do

---

[9] "Strike! Strike! Brothers, leave those rows."
[10] "Well, no, but . . ."
[11] "Wow, the police!"

it. (*Johnny turns and stands up against an imaginary wall, legs spread out, arms behind his back*)

SECRETARY: Oh no, we can't have arrests! We must maintain law and order.

SANCHO: But he's bilingual!

SECRETARY: Bilingual?

SANCHO: Simon que yes.[12] He speaks English! Johnny, give us some English. (*Snap*)

JOHNNY: (*Comes downstage*) Fuck you!

SECRETARY: (*Gasps*) Oh! I've never been so insulted in my whole life!

SANCHO: Well, he learned it in your school.

SECRETARY: I don't care where he learned it.

SANCHO: But he's economical!

SECRETARY: Economical?

SANCHO: Nickels and dimes. You can keep Johnny running on hamburgers, Taco Bell tacos, Lucky Larger beer, Thunderbird wine, yesca—

SECRETARY: Yesca?

SANCHO: Mota.

SECRETARY: Mota?

SANCHO: Leños [13] . . . *MARIJUANA*. (*Snap. Johnny inhales on an imaginary joint*)

SECRETARY: That's against the law!

JOHNNY: (*Big smile, holding his breath*) Yeah.

SANCHO: He also sniffs glue. (*Snap. Johnny inhales glue, big smile*)

JOHNNY: That's too much man, ese.

SECRETARY: No, Mr. Sancho, I don't think this—

SANCHO: Wait a minute, he has other qualities I know you'll love. For example an inferiority complex. (*Snap*)

JOHNNY: (*To Sancho*) You think you're better than me, huh ese? (*Swings switchblade*)

SANCHO: He can also be beaten and he bruises, cut him and he bleeds, kick him and he—(*He beats, bruises and kicks Pachuco*) Would you like to try it?

SECRETARY: Oh, I couldn't.

SANCHO: By my guest. He's a great scapegoat.

SECRETARY: No really.

SANCHO: Please.

SECRETARY: Well, all right. Just once. (*She kicks Pachuco*) Oh, he's so soft.

[12] yeah, sure
[13] "joints" of marijuana

SANCHO: Wasn't that good? Try again.

SECRETARY: (*Kicks Pachuco*) Oh, he's so wonderful! (*She kicks him again*)

SANCHO: Okay, that's enough, lady. You ruin the merchandise. Yes, our Johnny Pachuco model can give you many hours of pleasure. Why, the LAPD just bought twenty of these to train their rookie cops on. And talk about maintenance. Señorita, you are looking at an entirely self-supporting machine. You're never going to find our Johnny Pachuco model on the relief rolls. No, sir, this model knows how to liberate.

SECRETARY: Liberate?

SANCHO: He steals. (*Snap. Johnny rushes the secretary and steals her purse*)

JOHNNY: Dame esa bolsa, vieja! [14] (*He grabs the purse and runs. Snap by Sancho. He stops*)

(*Secretary runs after Johnny and grabs purse away from him, kicking him as she goes*)

SECRETARY: No, no, no! We can't have any *more* thieves in the State Administration. Put him back.

SANCHO: Okay, we still got other models. Come on, Johnny, we'll sell you to some old lady. (*Sancho takes Johnny back to his place*)

SECRETARY: Mr. Sancho, I don't think you quite understand what we need. What we need is something that will attract the women voters. Something more traditional, more romantic.

SANCHO: Ah, a lover. (*He smiles meaningfully*) Step right over here, Señorita. Introducing our standard Revolucionario and/or Early California Bandit type. As you can see he is well-built, sturdy, durable. This is the International Harvester of Mexicans.

SECRETARY: What does he do?

SANCHO: You name it, he does it. He rides horses, stays in the mountains, crosses deserts, plains, rivers, leads revolutions, follows revolutions, kills, can be killed, serves as a martyr, hero, movie star—did I say movie star? Did you ever see *Viva Zapata*? *Viva Villa, Villa Rides, Pancho Villa Returns, Pancho Villa Goes Back, Pancho Villa Meets Abbott and Costello*—

SECRETARY: I've never seen any of those.

SANCHO: Well, he was in all of them. Listen to this. (*Snap*)

---

[14] "Gimme that bag, old lady!"

REVOLUCIONARIO: (*Scream*) VIVA VILLAAAAA!

SECRETARY: That's awfully loud.

SANCHO: He has a volume control. (*He adjusts volume. Snap*)

REVOLUCIONARIO: (*Mousey voice*) viva villa.

SECRETARY: That's better.

SANCHO: And even if you didn't see him in the movies, perhaps you saw him on TV. He makes commercials. (*Snap*)

REVOLUCIONARIO: Is there a Frito Bandito in your house?

SECRETARY: Oh yes, I've seen that one!

SANCHO: Another feature about this one is that he is economical. He runs on raw horsemeat and tequila!

SECRETARY: Isn't that rather savage?

SANCHO: Al contrario,[15] it makes him a lover. (*Snap*)

REVOLUCIONARIO: (*To Secretary*) Ay, mamasota, cochota, ven pa'ca! (*He grabs Secretary and folds her back—Latin-lover style*)

SANCHO: (*Snap. Revolucionario goes back upright*) Now wasn't that nice?

SECRETARY: Well, it was rather nice.

SANCHO: And finally, there is one outstanding feature about this model I KNOW the ladies are going to love: he's a GENUINE antique! He was made in Mexico in 1910!

SECRETARY: Made in Mexico?

SANCHO: That's right. Once in Tijuana, twice in Guadalajara, three times in Cuernavaca.

SECRETARY: Mr. Sancho, I thought he was an American product.

SANCHO: No, but—

SECRETARY: No, I'm sorry. We can't buy anything but American-made products. He just won't do.

SANCHO: But he's an antique!

SECRETARY: I don't care. You still don't understand what we need. It's true we need Mexican models such as these, but it's more important that he be *American*.

SANCHO: American?

SECRETARY: That's right, and judging from what you've shown me, I don't think you have what we want. Well, my lunch hour's almost over, I better—

SANCHO: Wait a minute! Mexican but American?

SECRETARY: That's correct.

SANCHO: Mexican but . . . (*A sudden flash*) AMERICAN!

[15] on the contrary

Yeah, I think we've got exactly what you want. He just came in today! Give me a minute. (*He exits. Talks from backstage*) Here he is in the shop. Let me just get some papers off. There. Introducing our new 1970 Mexican-American! Ta-ra-ra-ra-rà-ra-ra-RA-RAAA!

(*Sancho brings out the Mexican-American model, a clean-shaven middle-class type in a business suit, with glasses*)

SECRETARY: (*Impressed*) Where have you been hiding this one?

SANCHO: He just came in this morning. Ain't he a beauty? Feast your eyes on him! Sturdy US STEEL frame, streamlined, modern. As a matter of fact, he is built exactly like our Anglo models except that he comes in a variety of darker shades: naugahyde, leather, or leatherette.

SECRETARY: Naugahyde.

SANCHO: Well, we'll just write that down. Yes, señorita, this model represents the apex of American engineering! He is bilingual, college educated, ambitious! Say the word "acculturate" and he accelerates. He is intelligent, well-mannered, clean—did I say clean? (*Snap. Mexican-American raises his arm*) Smell.

SECRETARY: (*Smells*) Old Sobaco, my favorite.

SANCHO: (*Snap. Mexican-American turns toward Sancho*) Eric? (*To Secretary*) We call him Eric Garcia. (*to Eric*) I want you to meet Miss JIM-enez, Eric.

MEXICAN-AMERICAN: Miss JIM-enez, I am delighted to make your acquaintance. (*He kisses her hand*)

SECRETARY: Oh, my, how charming!

SANCHO: Did you feel the suction? He has seven especially engineered suction cups right behind his lips. He's a charmer all right!

SECRETARY: How about boards, does he function on boards?

SANCHO: You name them, he is on them. Parole boards, draft boards, school boards, taco quality control boards, surf boards, two by fours.

SECRETARY: Does he function in politics?

SANCHO: Señorita, you are looking at a political MACHINE. Have you ever heard of the OEO, EOC, COD, WAR ON POVERTY? That's our model! Not only that he makes political speeches.

SECRETARY: May I hear one?

SANCHO: With pleasure. (*Snap*) Eric, give us a speech.

MEXICAN-AMERICAN: Mr. Congressman, Mr. Chairman,

members of the board, honored guests, ladies and gentlemen. (*Sancho and Secretary applaud*) Please, please. I
come before you as a Mexican-American to tell you
about the problems of the Mexican. The problems of
the Mexican stem from one thing and one thing alone:
he's stupid. He's uneducated. He needs to stay in school.
He needs to be ambitious, forward-looking, harder-work-
ing. He needs to think American, American, American,
AMERICAN, AMERICAN, AMERICAN. GOD
BLESS AMERICA! GOD BLESS AMERICA! GOD
BLESS AMERICA!! (*He goes out of control*)

(*Sancho snaps frantically and the Mexican-American finally
slumps forward, bending at the waist.*)

SECRETARY: Oh my, he's patriotic too!

SANCHO: Sí, señorita, he loves his country. Let me just
make a little adjustment here. (*Stands Mexican-American
up*)

SECRETARY: What about upkeep? Is he economical?

SANCHO: Well, no, I won't lie to you. The Mexican-American costs a little bit more, but you get what you pay for.
He's worth every extra cent. You can keep him running
on dry Martinis, Langendorf bread—

SECRETARY: Apple pie?

SANCHO: Only Mom's. Of course, he's also programmed to
eat Mexican food on ceremonial functions, but I must
warn you: an overdose of beans will plug up his exhaust.

SECRETARY: Fine! There's just one more question: HOW
MUCH DO YOU WANT FOR HIM?

SANCHO: Well, I tell you what I'm gonna do. Today and
today only, because you've been so sweet, I'm gonna let
you steal this model from me! I'm gonna let you drive
him off the lot for the simple price of—let's see taxes
and license included—$15,000.

SECRETARY: Fifteen thousand DOLLARS? For a MEXI-
CAN!

SANCHO: Mexican? What are you talking, lady? This is
a Mexican-American! We had to melt down two pachucos, a farm worker, and three gavachos to make this
model! You want quality, but you gotta pay for it! This
is no cheap run-about. He's got class!

SECRETARY: Okay, I'll take him.

SANCHO: You will?

SECRETARY: Here's your money.

SANCHO: You mind if I count it?

SECRETARY: Go right ahead.

SANCHO: Well, you'll get your pinkslip in the mail. Oh, do you want me to wrap him up for you? We have a box in the back.

SECRETARY: No, thank you. The governor is having a luncheon this afternoon, and we need a brown face in the crowd. How do I drive him?

SANCHO: Just snap your fingers. He'll do anything you want.

(*Secretary snaps. Mexican-American steps forward*)

MEXICAN-AMERICAN: RAZA QUERIDA, VAMOS LE-VANTANDO ARMAS PARA LIBERARNOS DE ESTOS DESGRACIADOS GABACHOS QUE NOS EXPLOTAN! VAMOS—[16]

SECRETARY: What did he say?

SANCHO: Something about lifting arms, killing white people, etc.

SECRETARY: But he's not suppose to say that!

SANCHO: Look, lady, don't blame me for bugs from the factory. He's your Mexican-American, you bought him, now drive him off the lot!

SECRETARY: But he's broken!

SANCHO: Try snapping another finger.

(*Secretary snaps. Mexican-American comes to life again*)

MEXICAN-AMERICAN: ESTA GRAN HUMANIDAD HA DICHO BASTA! Y SE A PUESTO EN MARCHA! BASTA! BASTA! VIVA LA RAZA! VIVA LA CAUSA! VIVA LA HUELGA! VIVAN LOS BROWN BERETS! VIVA LOS ESTUDIANTES! CHICANO POWER![17]

(*The Mexican-American turns toward the Secretary, who gasps and backs up. He keeps turning toward the Pachuco, Farm Worker and Revolucionario, snapping his fingers and turning each of them on, one by one*)

PACHUCO: (*Snap. To Secretary*) I'm going to get you, baby! VIVA LA RAZA!

FARM WORKER: (*Snap. To Secretary*) Viva la huelga! Viva la Huelga! VIVA LA HUELGA!

REVOLUCIONARIO: (*Snap. To Secretary*) Viva la revolucion!

---

[16] "Beloved Raza, let's pick up arms to liberate ourselves from those damned whites that exploit us! Let's go—"

[17] "This great mass of humanity has said enough! And it begins to march! Enough! Enough! Long live La Raza! Long live the Cause! Long live the strike! Long live the Brown Berets! Long live the students! Chicano Power!

VIVA LA REVOLUCIÓN!

(*The three models join together and advance toward the Secretary who backs up and runs out of the shop screaming. Sancho is at the other end of the shop holding his money in his hand. All freeze. After a few seconds of silence, the Pachuco moves and stretches, shaking his arms and loosening up. The Farm Worker and Revolucionario do the same. Sancho stays where he is, frozen to his spot*)

JOHNNY: Man, that was a long one, ese. (*Others agree with him*)

FARM WORKER: How did we do?

JOHNNY: Perty good, look all that lana, man! (*He goes over to Sancho and removes the money from his hand. Sancho stays where he is*)

REVOLUCIONARIO: En la madre, look at all the money.

JOHNNY: We keep this up, we're going to be rich.

FARM WORKER: They think we're machines.

REVOLUCIONARIO: Burros.

JOHNNY: Puppets.

MEXICAN-AMERICAN: The only thing I don't like is—how come I always got to play the goddamn Mexican-American?

JOHNNY: That's what you get for finishing high school.

FARM WORKER: How about our wages, ese?

JOHNNY: Here it comes right now. Three thousand dollars for you, three thousand dollars for you, three thousand dollars for you, and three thousand dollars for me. The rest we put back into the business.

MEXICAN-AMERICAN: Too much, man. Heh, where you vatos going tonight?

FARM WORKER: I'm going over to Concha's. There's a party.

JOHNNY: Wait a minute, vatos. What about our salesman? I think he needs an oil job.

REVOLUCIONARIO: Leave him to me.

(*The Pachuco, Farm Worker and Mexican-American exit, talking loudly about their plans for the night. The Revolucionario goes over to Sancho, removes his derby hat and cigar, lifts him up, and throws him over his shoulder. Sancho hangs loose, lifeless*)

REVOLUCIONARIO: (*To audience*) He's the best model we got! Ajua! (*Exit*)

No Saco Nada de la Escuela

Luis Valdez

1969

CHARACTERS: Francisco
                      Moctezuma
                      Malcolm
                      Florence
                      Abraham
                      Grade School Teacher
                      High School Teacher
                      Esperanza
                      College Professor
                      Nixon
                      Vato

FIRST PERFORMANCE: Centro Cultural Mexicano, St. John's Church Fresno, California

SCENE I: Elementary school.

School-yard sounds: children playing, shouting, laughing. (Four kids come running out: Florence, a white girl in pigtails and freckles; Malcolm, a black boy; then Francisco and Moctezuma, two Chicanitos)

ALL: (*A Cheer*) Yeah! Ring around the rosey, pocket full of posies, ashes, ashes, all fall down! Yeah! Let's do it again!

(Francisco has been watching from the side. He is grabbed by Florence and Monty, and pulled into circle, trying to get in step)

ALL: Ring around the rosey, pocket full of posies, ashes, ashes, we all fall down!
(Bell rings offstage)
FLORENCE: Oh! The bell!

[221]

(*They all jump to their places, and sit in two rows facing each other, two on each side*)

MONTY: Heh, look! Florence has a boyfriend! Florence has a boyfriend, yes un negro!

FLORENCE: No I don't. I don't have no boyfriend!

(*Teacher enters, short, bowlegged, old, ugly. She wears a white mask, and her feet stomp as she walks. She carries a huge pencil, two feet long, and a sign which she places on a stand at upstage center*)

TEACHER: (*Mimicking writing on blackboard*) Elementary A-B-C's.

(*Students begin to throw paper wads across room at one another*)

TEACHER: (*Turns, commands with high-pitched voice*) Children! I want those papers picked off the floor immediately!

(*Students run to pick up papers. Then sit down*)

TEACHER: There now, that's better. (*Her version of cheerfulness*) Good morning, class.

(*Class begins to sing except for Francisco, who looks at others bewildered. Teacher leads singing with her pencil*)

ALL: Good morning to you, good morning to you, good morning dear teacher, good morning to you.

TEACHER: That's fine. Now for roll call. Florence.

FLORENCE: Here teacher.

TEACHER: Malcolm.

MALCOLM: Yeow.

TEACHER: Moc—Moc— (*She can't pronounce Moctezuma*) Ramirez!

MONTY: Here.

TEACHER: Francisco.

FRANCISCO: Aquí.[1] (*Monty raises Francisco's hand*)

TEACHER: Abraham.

MONTY: Teacher, teacher. He's outside. He's a crybaby.

(*Abraham comes running out and runs across front stage, crying. He is dressed in cowboy boots, baseball cap on sideways, face is pale white with freckles*)

TEACHER: (*Helps him up*) There, there now, dear, don't cry. I want you to sit right there. (*Points to Monty*)

ABRAHAM: Wah! I can't sit there, he's brown.

MONTY: No, I'm not. (*Rubs forearm trying to remove color*)

[1] here

TEACHER: (*Turns him around*) Well, then I want you to sit right over there. (*Points towards Malcolm*)

ABRAHAM: Wah! I can't sit there, he's black.

TEACHER: Well, then do you see that nice little white girl over there? (*Points to Florence*) Would you like to sit there?

ABRAHAM: (*Man's voice*) Uh-huh!

TEACHER: Boy! (*Points to Malcolm*) You move (*Abraham sits next to Florence, Malcolm moves over by Monty and Francisco. They pantomine playing marbles*)

TEACHER: Now, all rise for the flag salute. (*Sweetly*) Stand up, Florence. Stand up, Abraham, dear. (*Turns to others, a bitch*) I said stand up!

(*Monty, Malcolm, and Francisco jump up and begin flag salute*)

ALL: I pledge allegiance to the flag . . .

(*Abe sneaks behind the teacher's back and pokes Francisco in the behind. Francisco thinks it was Monty and hits him, pushing him into Malcolm. They stand up straight again to continue and Abe sneaks over, again he pokes Francisco, who again pushes into Malcolm. Malcolm points to Abe. All three then attack Abe and throw him to the ground*)

TEACHER: (*Turns screaming*) Class; for heaven's sake! (*Abe, Monty, and Francisco run back to their seats*) Did they hurt you Abraham, dear? (*Turns to Monty and Francisco*) You should have more respect!

FRANCISCO: Pero, yo no hise nada.[2]

TEACHER: Shut up! (*Francisco cries*) Shut up! I said shut up! (*Francisco continues crying. Teacher kicks Francisco, who shuts up*)

TEACHER: (*Moves to center stage*) And now for our elementary A-B-C's. Florence, you're first.

FLORENCE: Here's an apple, teacher. (*Hands teacher apple*)

TEACHER: Thank you, dear.

FLORENCE: (*Moves downstage center*) A is for apple. B is for baby. And C is for candy. (*Pantomines licking sucker and skips back to her seat giggling*)

TEACHER: Very good! Now let's see who's next: Willie? (*She means Malcolm, who sits daydreaming*) Willie? (*Malcolm doesn't respond*) Willie! (*Teacher raises her voice. He still doesn't respond*) I meant you boy! (*Points at him*)

---

[2] "But I didn't do nothing."

MALCOLM: Teacher, my name ain't Willie. It's Malcolm.

TEACHER: It doesn't matter, boy. It doesn't matter. Do your ABC's.

MALCOLM: A is for Alabama. B is for banjo, and C is for cotton! (*Stamps foot, walks back to his seat. All the students are giggling*)

TEACHER: Not bad at all, boy, not bad at all. Let's see— who's next? Abraham dear? Say your ABC's.

ABRAHAM: A is for animal, and B is for . . . black and brown! (*Points to Monty and Francisco and Malcolm*)

TEACHER: Oh! He's able to distinguish his colors. Go on.

ABRAHAM: And C is for . . . for . . .

TEACHER: It has a "kuh," sound (*Meaning cat*)

ABRAHAM: Kill! (*Brightens up. Points to Francisco, Monty and Malcolm*)

TEACHER: Oh, no we mustn't say those things in class.

ABRAHAM: (*Crying*) I promise never to say it again. Teacher, look. (*Points upward. Teacher looks and Abe spits on Francisco, Monty, and Malcolm. They start to get up but are interrupted by Teacher*)

TEACHER: Ca-lass! Did you all know that Abraham here was named after one of our most famous presidents? Mr. Abraham Lincoln—the man who freed the slaves!

ALL: (*Aghast*) Gaw-leee!

TEACHER: After they were forced to pick cotton against their own free will.

ALL: Shame, shame, shame.

TEACHER: (*To Abraham*) Now, aren't you proud of your heritage?

ABRAHAM: A-huh. (*Laughing*)

TEACHER: (*To Abraham*) Of course, you are. Who's next. Moc . . . Moc . . . (*She can't pronounce his name*) Ramirez!

MONTY: Yes, teacher?

TEACHER: How do you pronounce your name?

MONTY: Moctezuma.

TEACHER: What?

MONTY: Moctezuma.

TEACHER: Oh! What a funny name! (*She laughs and class joins her. Teacher stomps foot and shuts them up*) Class! (*To Moctezuma*) And what ever does it mean?

MONTY: He was an emperor in the times of the Indians. He was a Mexican like me.

TEACHER: Oh! You mean Mon-tezuma.

MONTY: No, Moc-tezuma.

TEACHER: *Mon*tezuma.

MONTY: *Moc*tezuma.

TEACHER: *Mon*tezuma!

MONTY: *Moc*tezuma!

TEACHER: Montezuma! (*Begins to march up and down stage singing "MARINE HYMN"*) "From the halls of Monte-zoo-oo-ma to the shores of Tripoli." (*Using her oversized pencil as a bayonet, she stabs Monty who falls forward with head and arms hanging*) Now what's your name, boy? (*Lifts his head*)

MONTY: Monty.

TEACHER: Do your ABC's.

MONTY: A is for airplane, B is for boat, and C is for . . . ah, C is for . . . for . . . Cucaracha!

TEACHER: What!

MONTY: (*Crying*) Cuca—caca qui qui.

TEACHER: (*Twisting his ear*) What you meant to say was *cock-a-roach*, right?

MONTY: Sí.

TEACHER: What? (*Twists his ear even more*)

MONTY: Yes!

TEACHER: Yes, what?

MONTY: Yes, teacher!

TEACHER: Sit down. (*He sits down, crying*) And shut up! Let's see who's next. Oh, yes, Francisco.

FRANCISCO: Qué?

TEACHER: Oh! Another one that can't speak English! Why do they send these kids to me? You can't communicate with them. Is there anybody here that can speak Spanish?

MONTY: I can, teacher.

TEACHER: Tell him to do his ABC's.

MONTY: Dice que digas tus ABC's.[3]

FRANCISCO: Dile que no las sapo en ingles, nomas en español.[4]

MONTY: Teacher, he don't know how.

TEACHER: Oh, sit down! This has been a most trying day! Class dismissed . . . (*Students start to run out cheering*) except (*They freeze*) for Monty and Franky. (*Points to them. The rest of the class runs out*)

MALCOLM: (*Offstage*) You better give me that swing.

---

[3] "She says say your ABC's."
[4] "Tell her that I don't know them in English, only in Spanish."

ABRAHAM: (*Offstage*) No!

MALCOLM: (*Offstage*) I'm gonna hit you.

ABRAHAM: (*Offstage*) No.

(*Slap is heard and then Abraham wails*)

TEACHER: (*Teacher, Monty, and Francisco freeze until after the above, then they begin to move again*) Now look, boy. Tell him his name is no longer Francisco, but Franky.

MONTY: Dice que tu nombre ya no es Francisco, es Franky.⁵

FRANCISCO: No es Francisco . . . Panchito.

MONTY: Hey, teacher, he said his name is still Francisco. (*Francisco punches him in the back*)

TEACHER: Look, boy, Francisco—no, Franky—yes.

FRANCISCO: No, Francisco.

TEACHER: Franky!

FRANCISCO: Francisco.

TEACHER: Franky!!

FRANCISCO: O.K. (*As Teacher begins to walk away—to audience*) Francisco.

TEACHER: It's Franky!!!

FRANCISCO: (*Grabs sign and throws it on the ground*) Es Francisco, ya stufas.⁶

TEACHER: Oh! You nasty boy! (*Beats him over the head twice*) Remember the Alamo! (*Hits him again*) And just for that, you don't pass!

MONTY: Teacher, teacher, do I pass? (*Picks up sign, hands it to her*)

TEACHER: I suppose so. You are learning to speak English. (*To audience*) They shouldn't place these culturally deprived kids with the normal children. No, no, no. (*She leaves—stomps out. Monty begins to follow*)

FRANCISCO: (*Getting up from floor*) Oye, Moctezuma. ¿Que dijo esa vieja, chaparra y panzona?⁷

MONTY: Dijo que tu no pasates;⁸ you don't pass.

FRANCISCO: ¿Y tu pasates?

MONTY: Sure, I pass. I speak good English, and besides, my name isn't Moctezuma anymore . . . it's Monty.

FRANCISCO: No, es Moctezuma.

MONTY: Monty.

FRANCISCO: Moctezuma.

---

⁵ "She says that your name now isn't Francisco, it's Franky."
⁶ "It's Francisco, now stuff it!"
⁷ "Listen, Moctezuma, what did that paunchy old runt say?"
⁸ "She said you didn't pass."

MONTY: It's Monty. See, you stupid? You never learn. (*Sticks his tongue out at him and leaves*)

FRANCISCO: (*Crying*) Entonces dile a tu teacher que coma chet![9] (*Leaves crying*)

SCENE II: High school

Scene begins with same stand at center stage. (High school teacher—male, grey business suit, white mask—walks across stage, places high school sign on board)

STUDENTS: (*Backstage, singing*) Oh hail to thee, our Alma Mater, we'll always hold you dear. (*Then a cheer*) RAH, RAH, Sis boom bah! Sock it to them, sock it to them!

(*Florence enters stage right. Abraham enters stage left. His neck has a reddish tinge. He tries to hug Florence and is pushed away. He tries again and is pushed away. Florence continues walking*)

ABRAHAM: Where you going?

FLORENCE: To class.

ABRAHAM: What do you mean to class? I thought we were going steady.

FLORENCE: We *were* going steady.

ABRAHAM: (*Mimicking her*) What do you mean "We *were* going steady?"

FLORENCE: That's right. I saw you walking with that new girl Esperanza.

ABRAHAM: That Mexican chick? Aww, you know what I want from her. Besides, you're the only girl I love. I'll even get down on my knees for you. (*Falls on knees*)

FLORENCE: Oh! Abe, don't be ridiculous, get up.

ABRAHAM: (*Getting up*) Does that mean we're still going steady?

FLORENCE: I guess so.

ABRAHAM: Hot dog!

(*From stage right Francisco enters wearing dark glasses and strutting like a vato loco.*)

ABRAHAM: (*To Florence*) See that spic over there? Just to show you how much I love you, I'm gonna kick his butt!

FLORENCE: Oh, Abe, you can't be racist!

ABRAHAM: Get out of my way. (*Does warm up exercises like a boxer*)

(*Francisco has been watching him all along and has a knife in his hand, hidden behind his back so that it is not visible*)

ABRAHAM: Heh, greaser, spic!

[9] "Then tell your teacher to eat shit!"

FRANCISCO: (*Calmly*) You talking to me, vato?

ABRAHAM: You want some beef? (*Raises his fists*)

FRANCISCO: (*To audience*) Este vato quiere pedo. ¿Como la ven? Pos que le ponga! [10] (*Pulls out knife and goes after Abraham*)

ABRAHAM: (*Backing up*) Heh, wait a minute! I didn't mean it. I was only fooling. I— (*Francisco thrusts knife toward Abe. Florence steps in between and stops the knife by holding Francisco's arm. Action freezes*)

(*From stage right Malcolm jumps in and struts downstage. He wears a do rag on his head, and sun glasses. He bops around, snapping his fingers, walks up to Francisco and Abraham, looks at knife, feels the blade, and walks away as if nothing is happening. From stage right, Monty enters with his arm around Esperanza "Hopi." He runs up to Malcolm*)

MONTY: Hey, man, what's going on here?

MALCOLM: Say, baby, I don't know. I just don't get into these things. (*Moves away*)

MONTY: (*Stops him*) Hey, man, I said what's going on here?

MALCOLM: And I said I don't get into these things! What's the matter with you? Don't you understand? Don't you speak English?

MONTY: (*Angered*) You think you're better than me, huh? (*Monty grabs Malcolm by the throat, and Malcolm grabs him back. They start choking each other. Teacher enters stage center and observes the fight*)

MONTY: Nigger!

MALCOLM: Greaser!

MONTY: Blackie!

MALCOLM: Spic!

MONTY: Coon!

MALCOLM: Chili ass!

ESPERANZA: Oh, Monty, Monty!

TEACHER: Okay, that's enough. Cut it out, boys! We can settle this after school in the gym. We might even charge admission. Everyone to your seats.

(*Monty and Malcolm separate. Francisco puts his knife away, and all move back to their seats*)

TEACHER: Now, before we begin, I want to know who started that fight?

ABRAHAM: (*Innocently*) Mr. White? He did, sir.

---

[10] "This guy wants a scene. Like where? Then I'll give it to him."

FRANCISCO: (*Stands up*) I didn't start anything. He insulted me!

ABRAHAM: Who you going to believe—him or me? Besides, he pulled a knife.

TEACHER: (*To Francisco*) You did what? Get to the principal's office immediately!

FRANCISCO: Orale, but you know what? This is the last time I'm going to the principal's office for something like this. (*Exits mumbling*) Me la vas a pagar, ese, que te crees.[12]

TEACHER: I don't understand that boy. And he's one of the school's best athletes. (*Opens mouth, sudden realization. Runs to exit, shouts after Francisco*) Don't forget to show up for baseball practice. The school needs you.

FLORENCE: (*Stands*) Mr. White? I refuse to sit next to Abraham. He's a liar!

TEACHER: (*Stands next to Abraham*) Why, Florence, Abe here is the son of one of our best grower families.

FLORENCE: Well, I don't care if you believe me or not. But I refuse to sit next to a liar. (*Gives Abraham his ring*) And here's your ring!

TEACHER: All right, sit over here. (*Florence moves across stage and sits next to Esperanza. Francisco comes strutting in, whistling*) I thought I told you to go to the principal's office.

FRANCISCO: I did, man.

TEACHER: What did he say?

FRANCISCO: He told me not to beat on anymore of his gavachitos.[11] (*Taps Abraham on the head*)

TEACHER: (*Angered*) All right, sit over there. (*Indicates a spot beside Florence*) And you— (*Esperanza*) over here.

ESPERANZA: (*Stops beside Francisco at center stage*) You rotten pachuco. (*She sits beside Abraham*)

FRANCISCO: Uquela, esta ruca, man.[13] (*He sits beside Florence*)

TEACHER: Now, class, before we begin our high school reports, I'd like to introduce a new student. Her name is Esperanza Espinoza. (*He gives the pronunciation of her name with an Italian inflection*) It sounds Italian, I know, but I think she's Mexican-American. Isn't that right, dear?

[11] little Anglos
[12] "You'll pay for this, believe me."
[13] "Now there's a broad, man."

ESPERANZA: (*Self-consciously rising*) No, my parents were, but I'm Hawaiian. And you can just call me Hopi.

TEACHER: That's fine, Hopi. Now for our high school reports. Florence, you're first.

FLORENCE: (*Drumbeats. Florence walks to center stage, swaying hips like a stripper*) A is for achievement. B is for betterment. And C is for (*Bump and grind*) college! (*More drumbeats as she walks back to her seat*)

TEACHER: (*Impressed*) Well! It's good to see that you're thinking of your future. Let's see who's next? Oh yes, Willie.

MALCOLM: (*Hops to his feet*) I told you, man, my name ain't Willie. It's Malcolm!

TEACHER: All right, you perfectionist! Get up there and give your report.

MALCOLM: (*Struts to center stage. He begins to snap his fingers, setting a rhythm. Everybody joins in*) A is for Africa. B is for black like me. And C is community like black ghetto.

ALL: (*Still snapping to rhythm*) My goodness, Willie, you sure got rhythm. But then after all, all you people do. (*Three final snaps*)

TEACHER: Now then, Willie, about your report. The first two pages were fine, but that last part about the ghetto . . . don't you think it needs some improvement?

MALCOLM: You're telling me! Don't you think we know it?

TEACHER: Okay, that's a good C minus. Back to your seat. (*Malcolm sits down*) Abraham, up front!

ABRAHAM: Jabol mein fuehrer! (*Stomps to center stage*) A is for America: Love or Leave it! (*Francisco and Malcolm stand up to leave*)

TEACHER: Heh, you two! (*Motions for them to sit down*)

ABRAHAM: B is for better: better dead than Red. And C is for kill, kill, KILL! As in the United States Marine Corps. (*Snaps to attention*)

TEACHER: (*Marches up like a marine*) Very good, Abraham!

ABRAHAM: (*Saluting*) Thank you, sir.

TEACHER: That's an A plus, Abraham!

ABRAHAM: What did you expect, sir?

TEACHER: Dismissed! (*Abraham marches back to seat*) Monty, up front!

MONTY: Yes, sir! (*Marches sloppily to stage center. Salutes and freezes*)

TEACHER: (*With contempt*) Cut that shit out, and give your report.

MONTY: A is for American. B is for beautiful, like America the beautiful. And C is for country, like God Bless this beautiful American country! OOoooh, I love it. (*He falls to his knees, kisses the floor*)

TEACHER: (*Grabs Monty by the collar like a dog*) Here, have a dog biscuit. (*Monty scarfs up imaginary dog biscuit. Then is led back to his seat on all fours by teacher*) Now, who's next? Oh yes, Hopi.

ESPERANZA: (*Rises prissily, goes to center stage*) A is for Avon, as in "Ding Dong, Avon calling." B is for burgers which I love, and *beans,* which I hate! (*sneers at Francisco*) and C is for can't, as "I can't speak Spanish." And we have a new Buick Riviera, and my sister goes to the University of California, and we live in a tract home.

TEACHER: (*Leading her back to her seat*) Yes, dear! Just fine!

ESPERANZA: Really, really we do!

TEACHER: I believe you. That deserves a bean . . . uh, I means B plus (*Pause*) Now let's hear from . . . Franky?

FRANCISCO: Yeah, teach?

TEACHER: What do you mean "yeah, teach?" You know my name is Mr. White.

FRANCISCO: I know what your name is, ese. But you seem to forget that my name is Francisco, loco.

TEACHER: Get up there and give your report, you hoodlum.

FRANCISCO: Orale, ese vato, llévatela suave.[13] (*Moves to center stage*) A is for amor, como amor de mi Raza.

TEACHER: What!

FRANCISCO: B is for barrio como where the Raza lives. (*Teacher growls*) and C is carnalismo.

TEACHER: (*Heated*) How many times have I told you about speaking Spanish in my classroom, now what did you say?

FRANCISCO: Carnalismo.

TEACHER: (*At the limit of his patience*) And what does that mean?

FRANCISCO: Brotherhood.

TEACHER: (*Blows up*) GET OUT!

FRANCISCO: Why? I was only speaking my language. I'm a Chicano, que no?

TEACHER: Because I don't understand you, and the rest of the class doesn't understand you.

FRANCISCO: So what? When I was small I didn't understand English, and you kept flunking me and flunking me instead of teaching me.

[13] "Stay cool, man, take it easy."

TEACHER: You are permanently expelled from this high school!

FRANCISCO: Big deal! You call yourself a teacher? I can communicate in two languages. You can only communicate in one. Who's the teacher, teach? (*Starts to exit*)

MONTY: We're not all like that, teacher.

FRANCISCO: Tú te me callas el hosico.[14] (*Pushes Monty aside. Exits*)

TEACHER: That's the last straw! A is for attention. B is for brats like that. And C is for cut out. High school dismissed!

(*Teacher exits taking high school sign with him. Malcolm exits also, at opposite side of stage. Abraham, Florence, Esperanza and Monty rise, facing each other*)

MONTY: (*Looking at Florence*) Oh, Hopi?

ESPERANZA: (*Looking at Abraham*) Yes?

ABRAHAM: (*Looking at Esperanza*) Oh, Flo?

FLORENCE: (*Looking at Monty*) Yeah?

ABRAHAM AND MONTY: (*Together*) Do you wanna break up?

FLORENCE AND ESPERANZA: (*Together*) Yeah!

(*Monty takes Florence by the arm; Abraham takes Esperanza*)

MONTY: Oh boy, let's go to a party.

ABRAHAM: Let's go to a fiesta.

(*All exit*)

SCENE III: State college

Backstage sounds: police siren, shouts of "pigs off campus!"
(*College professor enters and places sign on stand. It reads "State College." Francisco enters pushing a broom*)

FRANCISCO: Oh, professor?

PROFESSOR: Yes?

FRANCISCO: I want to go to college.

PROFESSOR: Didn't you drop out of high school?

FRANCISCO: Simon, but I still want to go to college. I want to educate myself.

PROFESSOR: Well, that's tough. (*Exits*)

FRANCISCO: Pos mira que jijo . . .[15] (*Swings broom*)

(*Florence enters followed by Monty. Francisco freezes*)

FLORENCE: Guess what, folks? Monty and I are living together. Isn't that right, Monty?

MONTY: That's right, baby. Just me and you.

FLORENCE: Do you love me, Monty?

[14] "Shut your trap!"
[15] "Well look at that guy!"

MONTY: Oh, you know I do.

FLORENCE: Then come to momma!

MONTY: Ay mamasota, una gavacha! (*He runs over to her and begins to kiss her passionately*)

FLORENCE: (*Swooning*) Oh, you Latin lovers.

MONTY: (*Suddenly peeved*) Latin lovers? Your people have been oppressing my people for 150 years!

FLORENCE: Yes, Monty!

MONTY: You gavachas are all alike!

FLORENCE: (*The guilty liberal*) Oh yes, Monty!

MONTY: And that's why I'm going to give it to you! (*Rolls up his sleeve, clenches fist*) Right between the you-know-what's. (*Grabs her and begins to kiss her again passionately*) Viva Zapata!! (*Makes out again*) Viva Villa!!! (*Raises fist*) Viva la Revolución!!! (*Wraps a leg around her, kisses her. Then falls to the floor exhausted*)

FLORENCE: (*Sitting on his back*) Oh, Monty. You do that so well.

MONTY: (*Puffing underneath*) Shut up. While my people are starving in the barrio, your people are sitting fat and reech.

FLORENCE: Reech?

MONTY: Rich! Rich, you beech. Oh, my accent sleeped . . . slopped, sloped! What am I saying?

FLORENCE: (*Noticing Francisco*) Monty, look: a chicken-o.

MONTY: A what?

FLORENCE: A Mexican-American?

MONTY: What?

FLORENCE: An American of Mexican descent?

MONTY: I'm going to give you one more chance. I'm going to spell it out for you. (*Spells out C-h-i-c-a-n-o in the air*) What's this?

FLORENCE: (*Reading his movements*) C!

MONTY: And this and this? (*H and I*)

FLORENCE: C-H-I . . . Chic! Chica . . . oh, Chicano! Chicano! (*Jumps up and down*)

MONTY: Good! Now get out. And don't come back until I call you. (*Florence exits*) 'Cause this is a job for . . . Supermacho! (*Approaches Francisco, Anglo accent to his Spanish*) ¿Qué-hubole, esay bato loco? [16] Heh, don't I know you?

FRANCISCOS ¿Qué nuevas? [17]

MONTY: Isn't your name Francisco?

[16] "What's up, Dude?"
[17] "What's new"

FRANCISCO: Simon.

MONTY: You're wanted.

FRANCISCO: No, I'm not! (*Begins to run across stage*)

MONTY: For our program. (*Stops Francisco*)

FRANCISCO: What program?

FLORENCE: (*Sticking her head out from back stage*) Now Monty?

MONTY: No, not yet. (*Turns to Francisco*) Hey man, you know La Raza is getting together! You know we have 300 years of Chicano culture? You know our women are beautiful?! Just look at them, mamasotas!

FRANCISCO: Simon, estan a toda madre.

MONTY: Pero primero necesitamos unos cuantos gritos como los meros machos. Mira fijate, Que Viva La Raza! [18] (*Francisco repeats*) Que Viva La Causa! (*Francisco repeats*) Que Viva la Huelga! (*Francisco repeats*)

FLORENCE: (*Enters*) Look, Monty, I'm getting tired of waiting, godamit!

MONTY: (*Turns to Florence*) Okay, just wait a minute. Just one more. (*Turns to Francisco*) ¿Uno mas pero este con muchos tu sabes que, eh? [19] Que Viva La Revolución!

FRANCISCO: ¿La revolución . . . ? (*Looks at Flo*) Pos que viva—y a comenzar con esa gavacha, jija de la . . .[20]

MONTY: Hey, wait a minute man. That's not where it's at, vato. This is what you call "universal love." I don't think you're ready for college. (*Florence jumps on Monty's back*) And when you are, come look me up at the Mexican Opportunity Commission Organization: MOCO. And I'm the Head Moco. Chicano Power, carnal! (*Exits*)

FRANCISCO: (*To audience*) No, hombre, esta mas mocoso que la . . .[21]

(*Hopi and Abraham enter stage left. Abraham is wearing a ten-gallon hat*)

ESPERANZA: Guess what folks? Abraham and I are engaged. Isn't that right, Abraham?

ABRAHAM: That's right, baby. Just me and you. (*He leans her over to kiss her*)

ESPERANZA: (*Snapping back up. To Francisco*) What are you looking at?

FRANCISCO: Oh! ¿Esperanza, no te acuerdas de mi? [22]

[18] "But first we need a few shouts like real men. Look, long live . . ."

[19] One more, but this one full of you know what, huh?"

[20] So, long live—let's begin with that Anglo, daughter of a . . ."

[21] "No, man, it's snottier than . . ."

[22] "don't you remember me?"

ESPERANZA: My name is Hopi.

FRANCISCO: Orale, esa, no te . . .[23]

ESPERANZA: And don't call me *esa!*

ABRAHAM: Is that Mexican bothering you?

ESPERANZA: Just ignore him, sugar plum, just ignore him. (*They move stage right*)

ABRAHAM: Do you know that my dad owns two hundred thousand acres of lettuce in the Salinas Valley?

ESPERANZA: Really!

ABRAHAM: And he has two hundred dumb Mexicans just like him working for him.

ESPERANZA: Really!

ABRAHAM: My daddy's a genius!

ESPERANZA: Oh! You're so smart! You're so intelligent! Oh, you white god, you! (*Bows falling on her knees in worship*)

ABRAHAM: Shucks. You don't have to do that. Why, you remind me of the little brown squaw my pappy used to have.

ESPERANZA: Squaw! (*Getting up in anger*)

ABRAHAM: Don't get mad, my little taco. My little tamale. My little frijol. (*Pronounced free hole*)

FRANCISCO: Free hole?

ABRAHAM: Besides, I've got a surprise for you. Why, just the other day my pappy made me president.

ESPERANZA: President?

ABRAHAM: President!

ESPERANZA: Of the company?

ABRAHAM: Of the Future Farmers of America.

ESPERANZA: (*Disappointed*) Oh, Abraham.

FRANCISSCO: (*Laughing, moves up to Hopi*) ¿Oyes, por eso venistes al colegio? ¿A toparte con un pendejo? [24]

ESPERANZA: Well, at least he's not out on the corner pushing dope.

ABRAHAM: You Mexicans ought to be out in the fields.

ESPERANZA: (*To Abraham*) You tell him, sugar.

FRANCISCO: That's all you think I can do, huh? Well I'm gonna go to college on the E.O.P. program!

ESPERANZA Look. I made it through college without any assistance. I don't see why you can't.

FRANCISCO: (*Mimics her*) I made it through college . . .

(*Professor enters stage center, Monty and Florence enter stage right*)

[23] "Listen, you, don't you . . ."
[24] "Listen, for that you came to college? To run into a dum-dum?"

PROFESSOR: Ladies and gentlemen, can we prepare for our college seminar? (*Spots Francisco*) Aren't you the custodian?

FRANCISCO: Yes, but, a . . . Monty wants to talk to you.

MONTY: Oh, sir, we thought we might be able to get him in under MOCO, you know, Mexican Opportunity Commission Organization?

PROFESSOR: Now look, Monty, we got you in here, and unless you want to be out, get back into your place. (*To Francisco*) No, I'm sorry, there's no room. No room! (*Pushing him out*)

FRANCISCO: I want to go to college!

PROFESSOR: These students, they don't understand. (*To audience*) They don't realize that there is no room in our college, no room at all. In this college there is not room for one more student—not one more *minority* student.

(*Malcolm enters stage right wearing a black shirt, black leather jacket, and black beret. He is carrying a rifle. Abraham begins to shake and point at him*)

PROFESSOR: (*To Abraham*) I'll handle it. (*Moves over to Malcolm*) Pardon me, boy, but are you registered? (*Malcolm cocks rifle, Professor looks at rifle chamber, looks at Malcolm, looks at audience*) He's registered.

ALL: He registered.

FRANCISCO: (*Peeking back in*) ¿Vistes eso, Moctezuma? [25]

PROFESSOR: No, no, out! Out! (*Moctezuma helps Professor push Francisco out*)

MONTY: (*Pushes him out*) I'll see that it doesn't happen again, sir.

PROFESSOR: Well, see that it doesn't. Now class, in order to qualify for graduation; you must deliver one final report. And it must be concise, logical, and have conviction. Miss Florence, you're first.

FLORENCE: A is for anti as in anti-war. B is for Berkeley as in anti-war Berkeley. And C is for chick as in anti-war Berkeley chick.

PROFESSOR: Well, that was a very personal and revealing account, Miss Florence, and that should qualify you for . . .

ABRAHAM: That stunk!! And if you pass her, I'll have your job. Remember, you're working for my daddy!

MONTY: Oh, sir, please give her one more chance.

PROFESSOR: Yes, just get back to your seat, Monty. I was

[25] "Did you see that, Moctezuma?"

about to say that it lacked conviction. Try again, Miss Florence. (*Stands next to her*)

FLORENCE: A is for adult.

PROFESSOR: A-huh.

FLORENCE: B is for become, as to become an adult.

PROFESSOR: It happens to the best of us.

FLORENCE: And C is for cop out, as to become an adult and cop out.

PROFESSOR: That is the American way, Miss Florence. You will graduate! Let's see who's next . . . Malcolm.

MALCOLM: (*Moves forward menacingly*) A is for Afro, as in Afro-American. B is for black, as in Afro-American Black Panther. And C is for Cleaver, Eldridge Cleaver, Afro-American, Black Panther! (*Gives Panther salute*)

PROFESSOR: Well, I see the logic but I don't like it.

MALCOLM: Good, that's the way we want it!

PROFESSOR: All right! All right! You'll graduate.

ABRAHAM: He graduates?? (*He begins to pantomime different ways of killing Malcolm—machine gun, grenades, airplane, and finally builds a rocket*) A is for anti- (*Puts first stage on missile*) B is for ballistic (*Builds second stage*) and M is for missile. (*Puts final stage on missile*) (*During the above, Malcolm has just been standing, cool and collected, Everybody but Malcolm begins the count-down*)

ALL: 5-4-3-2-1 Fire! (*They make whistling noise of a rocket in the air. As the rocket lands with a loud noise, Malcolm turns around and points gun at Abraham*)

ABRAHAM: (*Scared like a boy*) A is for animal. B is for back off. And C is for coward, Mama! (*Exits*)

PROFESSOR: Abraham, come back!

(*Francisco enters stage left dressed as a Brown Beret, with rifle in hand*)

FRANCISCO: ¿Ya ves Moctezuma? (*Monty tries to push him out but is thrown back*) Un lado!

PROFESSOR: Just a minute! Just a minute! (*To Francisco*) You want to go to college? What are your qualifications?

FRANCISCO: My qualifications? Pos mira que hijo de . . .[26] (*Pulls back rifle into position to hit Professor from the front and Malcolm pokes his gun at his back. They freeze and Esperanza walks over and moves around Francisco, checking him out. She moves back to her place*)

PROFESSOR: (*Jumps up and they unfreeze*) All right, you're in!

[26] "Look, son of a . . ."

FRANCISCO: Where do I sit?

PROFESSOR: Over there! (*Frantically*) This is getting out of hand. MONTY, Monty, my boy, your report.

MONTY: A is for American like a Mexican-American.

PROFESSOR: Wonderful!

MONTY: And B is for bright, like a bright Mexican-American.

PROFESSOR: Great! Great!

MONTY: And C is for comprado [27] like a bright, Mexican-American comprado.

PROFESSOR: Bought and sold! Monty, my boy, you will graduate. Congratulations! And as you go forward into this great society, I want you to remember one thing. (*Points forward*) I want you always to move forward, move forward in that great American tradition. (*Monty has been looking to where the Professor has been pointing, gets scared, and sneaks off to his place, moving backward*) Forever forward. (*Looks around when he realizes that Monty has left*) Monty, Monty! (*Getting hysterical*) Oh! This is getting out of hand! Out of hand! Let's see. Oh, yes, Hopi?

ESPERANZA: (*Esperanza has been talking to Francisco and now has her arms around his neck*) Who?

PROFESSOR: (*Scared*) Hopi?

ESPERANZA: My name is Esperanza, you marrano! [28]

PROFESSOR: Your report, please.

ESPERANZA: Orale, llévatela suave. (*Walks 'chuca fashion to center stage*) A is for action, as in accion social. B is for batos, as in accion social de batos. And C is for Chicana as in Accion Social de Batos y Chicanas. (*Francisco lets out with a grito*)

FRANCISCO: ¿Y ahora que dices, MOC-tezuma? [29]

PROFESSOR: All right, Francisco, your report.

FRANCISCO: Hey, wait a minute, man. I just got in here.

MONTY: What's the matter? Can't do it, huh?

PROFESSOR: (*Regaining a sense of authority*) Is that your problem, boy, can't you do it?

FRANCISCO: Yes, I can! And don't call me boy!

PROFESSOR: (*Cringes in fear again*) Fine, fine.

FRANCISCO: A is for advanced, as the advanced culture of indigenous American Aztlan. B is for bronce as the ad-

[27] sellout
[28] riff-raff
[29] "And now what do you say . . . ?"

vanced culture of indigenous American Aztlan which brought bronze civilization to the Western Hemisphere. And C is for century, as the advanced culture of indigenous American Aztlan which brought bronze civilization to the Western Hemisphere and which, more over, will create el nuevo hombre [30] in the twenty-first century, El Chicano. Give me my diploma.

PROFESSOR: Just a minute, hold it right there! (*Goes to side and grabs book*) I have here in my hand the book of American knowledge. There is nothing in here about As-ta-lan, nothing in here about Chicken-O. In fact there is nothing in here about nothing, and as you can see— (*Turns book toward the audience, there is a dollar sign printed on page*) This is the honest truth which is close to all of our American hearts. No, I'm sorry, but under the circumstances I don't think that you will (*Francisco has gun in his face, and Malcolm puts his rifle to his back*) be here next year, because you will graduate. (*Malcolm and Francisco move to their places*) And now, students, line up for that golden moment, graduation! And here to present the awards, on this fine day, is none other than that great statesman, that golden-mouthed orator, that old grape sucker himself, the President of the United States, Mr. Richard M. Nixon. (*Nixon moves in from stage right. He is wearing cap and gown, giving peace symbol. Shakes hands with the Professor*) A few words, please, Mr. President.

NIXON: I'd like to say just three things today, only three. First, don't forget that great American dollar which put you through college. (*Applause*) Second, always kiss ass; and third, eat plenty of Salinas scab lettuce!

PROFESSOR: Thank you, Mr. President. Now, if you'll just step this way, we shall begin the awards. First, we have Miss Florence, a fine girl.

(*Miss Florence moves to center stage, receives diploma. Nixon places a graduation cap on her head. Cap comes with white hood, which covers her head completely. She moves back to her place*)

PROFESSOR: Next we have, Monty. Good boy. (*Monty walks up and kisses the president's hand. Then he places cap over his own head, goes back to his place*) Next is Willie.

PRESIDENT: Here we are, Willie.

MALCOLM: (*Takes diploma*) My name is Malcolm, you

[30] the new man (an abstraction)

white mutha— (*President and Professor duck*)

PRESIDENT: And here's your white bag.

MALCOLM: I don't need that.

PROFESSOR: But what are you going to do without it?

MALCOLM: You're going to find out. (*He walks to stage right—whistles*) Come here, baby. (*Florence takes off her cap, moves to center stage, throws cap on floor, walks off stage with Malcolm*)

PRESIDENT: A militant!

PROFESSOR: That's okay. There's a whole lot of them that aren't. Next we have Francisco. (*Francisco moves up, takes diploma, moves quickly back to his place. President tries to put cap on him, misses, and almost falls on Esperanza. He backs off cautiously*)

PRESIDENT: Speed, these Mexicans. Fast!

PROFESSOR: Next, we have Esperanza. (*She moves to center stage, takes diploma*)

PRESIDENT: And here's your white bag.

ESPERANZA: I DON'T need your white bag!

PRESIDENT: But you can't exist in our society without one.

PROFESSOR: What are you going to do without your white bag?

(*From audience someone gets up and yells*: "Hey, I want to go to college.")

ESPERANZA: That's what I'm going to do. I'm going to help my carnales get into college.

VATO: Ayúdenme! [31] (*Runs toward stage*)

PROFESSOR: No!

(*Francisco and Esperanza try to help Vato from audience. There's tug of war*)

VATO: Sí (*With Francisco and Esperanza*)

PROFESSOR: No!

VATO: Sí!

PROFESSOR: No!

VATO: Si! (*He jumps up onstage, pushing Professor back. Vato waves to audience and yells*) Orale, I made it into college. (*Gives Chicano handshake to Francisco and Esperanza*)

PRESIDENT: Well, I see that my job here is done. I shall now take my students—student . . . into the great white world. Right face! Forward march! (*Exits stage right followed by Monty*)

[31] "Help me!"

FRANCISCO: Moctezuma! ¡Qué date con tu Raza! [32]

ESPERANZA: Ah, let him go. There's more where he came from.

FRANCISCO: Pos que le pongan! (*Students start coming in from all sides of stage. Everyone starts pointing at Professor, yelling*) Teach us. Teach us!

PROFESSOR: Just a minute. Just a minute (*To audience*) So many brown faces, brown minds, brown ideas, what is this . . . a chocolate factory? (*Everybody jumps at him*) I'm going to a college where they understand. Where they appreciate good white professors, where there won't be any Chicanos . . . like Fresno State College. (*Or whichever college is appropriate*) President Baxter, HELP! (*Exits stage right*)

VATO: Orale, una colecta!

(*Everyone starts looking for change. Vato begins to take collection*)

FRANCSCO: ¿Colecta? ¿Pera qué?

FIRST NEW STUDENT: La birria.

SECOND NEW STUDENT: La mota.

THIRD NEW STUDENT: El wine.

FRANCISCO: ¿Por no estan bien calabasas? Estamos en colegio. Hay que aprender de nuestra cultura, nuestra Raza, de Aztlan. [33]

VATO: (*Turns to next student*) But who's going to teach us? (*They move on down the line asking each other the same question*)

ESPERANZA: (*Last in line asks Francisco*) Who's going to teach us?

FRANCISCO: Who's going to teach us?

ALL: Our own people! (*They point at audience*)

FRANCISCO: Entonces ¿qué se dice? Viva . . ! [34]

ALL: La Raza!

FRANCISCO: Viva!

ALL: La Huelga!

FRANCISCO: Chicano!

ALL: Power!

(*Actors get audience to shout "Chicano power." Then all sing "Bella Ciao"*)

[32] "Stay with your race."

[33] "Aren't you flunkouts? We are in college. You must learn about our culture. Our race. About Aztlan."

[34] "Then what do you say? Long live . . ."

Bibliography

Alurista, "When Raza?" *Floricanto*. Los Angeles: Centro de Estudios Chicanos, 1971.

————, "In the Barrio Sopla El Viento." *Floricanto*. Los Angeles: Centro de Estudios Chicanos, 1971.

————, "Must be the Season of the Witch." *Floricanto*. Los Angeles: Centro de Estudios Chicanos, 1971.

————, "En el Barrio." *Florencanto*. Los Angeles: Centro de Estudios Chicanos, 1971.

————, "Fruto de Bronce." *Floricanto*. Los Angeles: Centro de Estudios Chicanos, 1971.

————, "Can this Really be the End?" *Floricanto*. Los Angeles: Centro de Estudio Chicanos, 1971.

Barrio, Raymond, *The Plum Plum Pickers*. Sunnyvale, California: Ventura Press, 1971.

Brito, Aristeo, Jr., "El Peregrino." Mimographed, 1971.

[Delgado], Abelardo, *Chicano: 25 Pieces of a Chicano Mind*. n. p; n.d.

Duran, Marcus, "Retrato de un Bato Loco." *Con Safos*, 5 (1970).

"El Chapo," "Chavalo Encanicado." *Con Safos*, 7 (1971).

Elias, Leonardo, "Aztec Mother." Unpublished poem, in a letter to D. Harth, 1972.

Galarza, Ernesto, *Barrio Boy*. Notre Dame, Ind.: Notre Dame University Press, 1969.

Gomez, Manuel, "No Se Puede Olvidar." *El Ombligo*. San Diego, Calif: Centro de Estudios Chicanos Publications, 1971.

Gonzalez, Jorge, "A Delano," *El Ombligo*. San Diego, Calif.: Centro de Estudios Chicanos Publications 1971.

Kirach, Gallo, "Tecatos," *El Ombligo*. San Diego.: Centro de Estudios Chicanos Publications, 1971.

Lopez, Cesar, "Católicos por La Raza," *El Ombligo*. San Diego, Calif.: Centro de Estudios Chicanos Publications, 1971.

Muro, Amado, "Sunday in Little Chihuahua." *New Mexico Quarterly*, Autumn (1965).

————., "María Tepache." *Arizona Quarterly*, 4 (1969).

Ortega, Jerónimo G., "Blue Bike Brings a Blue Day." *Con Safos*, 6 (1970).

Perez, Gloria, "Mi Hombre," *El Ombligo*. San Diego, Calif.: Centro de Estudios Chicanos Publications, 1971.

Rivera, Tomas, "On the Road to Texas: Pete Fonseca." Translated by Maria Ortiz. By permission of author.

Salinas, Omar, "Robstown," *Crazy Gypsy*. Fresno, Calif.: Origines, 1970.

————., "Aztec Angel." *Crazy Gypsy*. Frenso, Calif.: Origines, 1970.

Salinas, Raúl R., "Journey II." Leavenworth, Kansas: *Aztlán* III, March (1971).

Sánchez, Ricardo, "Migrant Lament. . . ." *Canto y Grito Mi Liberación*. El Paso, Texas: Mictla, 1970.

————., "It Is Urgent," *Canto y Grito Mi Liberación*. El Paso, Texas: Mictla, 1970.

Suarez, Mario, "El Hoyo." *Arizona Quarterly*, 3 (1947).

Valdez, Luis, "The Actos," *El Teatro Campesino*. Fresno, Calif.: Cucaracha Press, 1971.

————., "No Saco Nada de la Escuela," *El Teatro Campesino*. Fresno, Calif: Cucaracha Press, 1971.

————., "Los Vendidos," *El Teatro Campesino*. Fresno, Calif.: Cucaracha Press, 1971.

Vasquez, Richard, *Chicano*. New York: Doubleday, 1970.

Villarreal, Jose Antonio, *Pocho*. New York: Doubleday, 1970.

"Zeta," "Perla Is a Pig." *Con Safos*, 5 (1970).

Glossary

¡Ay va por ustedes!	"This is for you" (as in a toast).
Bato or *Vato*	Guy, dude, man (slang).
Blanquillos	Eggs.
Bote	Marijuana. Also jail (slang), or "can".
Cabrón	Literally, a he-goat; cuckold, sometimes used as a coarse expression of endearment similar to "You cute little bastard." Also used in a pejorative sense.
Café con Leche	Coffee with milk.
¡Cállense!	Shut up!
Carga	Heroin (slang).
Carnal	Brother (slang).
Casucha	Hut, shack.
¡Cómo eres escandaloso!	You are really scandalous.
Contemplando las moscas	Literally, "Contemplating flies"; doing nothing.
Corridas	Bullfights.
Chale	No, nix (slang).
Chamacos	Boys.
Champurrado	A beverage made with sweetened cornmeal.
Chavalo	Boy, kid.
Chavalona	Girl, kid.
Chicharrones	Deep-fried pork rinds.
Chile Bravo	A red-hot chili pepper.
Chilpayates	Little kids, brats (slang).
Chirinoleras	Tattlers, gossips.
Chiva	Heroin: see also *carga*.
Chones	Panties.

Derechazos	A bullfighting pass.
Encanicado	Moonstruck, passionately in love.
En Nuestros Tiempos	In our times.
Era	He was.
Ésa es Mecha	This is hot like a match (idiomatic).
Ese	A slang form of address common to the vato dialect, literally "that one," or "you."
Estropajo	Rag.
Farol de rodillas	A bullfighting movement.
Fritanga	Fried food.
Geeze	To inject heroin (slang).
Gorditas	Thick-filled tortillas.
Hay, ¡que sí estaban buenas!	Boy, were they ever good!
Hay [ay] *te watcho, vato.*	See you later, dude (slang).
Helote (ELOTE)	A corncob.
Hijo	Son.
¡Híjola!	Wow!
[H] *órale loco*	OK, break! (slang).
Ixtle	A cactus fiber, often woven into bags.
Largo (sic) *cordobesa*	A bullfighting pass.
Lasernista	Another bullfighting movement.
Mamasita	Sweet or hot mama.
Manoletina	A bullfighting pass attributed to the famous Manolete.
Manso	A domesticated animal or a docile person.
Me lleva a la . . .	Well, I'll be a . . .
Menudo	Tripe stew. Often used as a folk cure for a hangover.
Mi primo Tudi es muy gacho	My cousin Tudi is quite a square.
Montera	The bicornered hat worn by matadors.
Muchachitos	Boys or children.
Muchachos	Boys.
Muleta	The matador's red cape.
Muy apurado	In a hurry, very pressed.
Nalgas razgadas	Bruised buttocks.

Nel	No.
Nopalitos	Fried cactus.
Novilleros	Novice bullfighters.
Novillos	Young bulls.
Órale	Listen, OK, or "Stop fooling around" (slang).
Pachanga	A party.
Pancitas	Bits of bread.
Pansona (*sic*) (*Panzona*)	Pregnant.
Paseo de pecho	A bullfighting pass.
Pendejo	Pubic hair; figuratively, a stupid or worthless person.
¡Pinchis pollos!	Damn chickens! variant: pinches.
Pollo	Chicken. *Pollo en Mole*: chicken in red chili sauce.
Por favor	Please.
Primo	Cousin.
¡Qué caray!	My gosh!
¡Qué gacho!	What a bummer!
¿Qué pasa?	What's happening?
¡Qué vida!	What a life!
Refín	Food, "chow."
Simón	Yes.
Sinvergüenza	Shameless one.
Somberote	A ridiculous hat. Variant: sombrerote.
Tamales de dulce	Sweet tamales.
Tambache	A flour tortilla.
Tapatío	A person from Guadalajara or Jalisco, Mexico.
Tepache	A drink made of pulque, water, pineapple, and cloves.
Tía	Aunt. *Tío*, uncle.
¿Tú sabes?	Do you know what I mean?
Vecino	Neighbor.
¡Ven acá!	Come here! (familiar imperative).
Viejitas	Old women.
Viejito	Little old one; Pop, Dad.